Units of Measurement

INTRODUCTION TO THE
INTERNATIONAL SYSTEM OF UNITS
[SI]
SYSTÈME INTERNATIONAL D'UNITÉS

Conversion Factors
Definitions and
Tables of Equivalents

Revised and Enlarged Edition

Additional copies of this handbook are available by purchase from the publisher at the following address:

J.A.M. Gaboury
P.O. Box 24, Station "B"
Montréal (Québec) Canada   H3B 3J5

OFFICE:

10115 Garnier Street
Montréal   H2C 3B8
Tel.: (514) 388-1926

All inquiries should be addressed to:
J.A.M. Gaboury, D.Sc., M.C.I.C.
P.O. Box 24, Station "B"
Montréal (Québec) Canada   H3B 3J5

Legal deposit: first quarter 1991

Printed in Canada

(Serial No. 91)

The International System of Units or "Le Système International d'Unités" which is officially abbreviated as [SI] in all languages is a modernized metric system.

SI is the third major development of the metric system. From the original, mainly practical system, came the centimetre-gram-second (cgs) system. The rapid growth of science in the nineteenth century, particularly in the fields of electricity and magnetism, made further revision necessary and led to the establishment of the metre-kilogram-second (MKS) system, to which a fourth unit, the ampere, was added, so that it became known as the MKSA system. Further rationalisation, and the addition of two new units, the kelvin (thermodynamic temperature) and the candela (luminous intensity) led to its being re-named the International System of Units. A seventh unit, the mole, measuring amount of substance in chemistry, was subsequently added.

This process of evolution has yielded various systems of units. Some of these units are gradually declining in use, because they have either served the purpose for which they were designed or are being replaced with SI units. The introduction of the SI did not eliminate all of the units previously employed. Several units of measure — because of their practical importance or because of their use in specialized fields — will not be changed. Time will continue to be measured in hour, minutes and seconds; and the electricity we consume will continue to be measured in watts.

The increasing popularity of the International System of Units has created many problems of conversion for scientists, engineers, technicians, teachers, manufacturers and those engaged in the international trade. This book is designed to assist them in overcoming the obstacles presented by conflicting systems.

The present edition, has been revised and expanded to conform to practices recommended, approved and adopted by the various international standardisation bodies, such as the General Conference of Weights and Measures (CGPM) and the International Organization for Standardization (ISO).

J.A.M. G.

CONTENTS

ADDENDA

In going metric there will be an inevitable transition period during which both the old and the new systems of measurement will be encountered in all work situations.

As early as possible in the change-over period, therefore, it will be advisable to start "thinking metric" — that is to start "getting a feel" for the length of a centimetre, the weight (mass) of a kilogram, the distance in kilometres a car will run on 30 litres of "super" and so on. As soon as these new measurements begin to have meaning for us, we will start using them in discussions, and when remembering facts and figures. The first aim of this book is, then, to introduce the metric system, and to interpret it in terms that are relevant to daily living.

We must realize, though, that the old measurements will be with us for a long time yet. Most of the books in libraries, reference standards, old title deeds, and so on, will, of course, carry the present measurements, although we ourselves will cease to use them in ordinary circumstances, and our children will no longer learn them at school. The perch, the chain, the hundredweight, the quart, and other measurements may soon be almost as forgotten as the cubit, league, or barleycorn now are. But when we do come across them, it will be necessary to know how to convert them to metric measurements in order to understand them. Consequently, the second purpose of this book is to provide a handy set of comparisons between the various types of measurements — the archaic ones, those used at the moment, and the metric measurements that are about to take over.

Symbols and Conventions

Unit Names

1. Use, if possible, only those units which are ranged in multiples or submultiples of one thousand (10^3) relative to each other and to the base unit,

    e.g.   use megametre (10^6);   kilometre (10^3);   metre (10^0);
    millimetre (10^{-3});   micrometre (10^{-6});   nanometre (10^{-9}).

This makes for simplicity and reduces the likelihood of error in calculations, since an error 1000 times too big or too small is easier to detect than an error of 10 only. Exceptions may be made if the unit is already in wide use (such as centimetre) or is otherwise convenient.

2. Choose whichever multiple or submultiple allows you to express the value you want in not more than three (3) integers, unless another unit is convenient for purposes of comparison.

    e.g.   12 kN   rather than   12 000 N   or 1.2×10^4 N
    10.5 mm   "   "   0.0105 m   " 1.05×10^{-2} m
    1401 Pa   "   "   1.401 kPa   " 1.401×10^3 Pa

But for ready comparison it would be sensible to say that a force of 12 kN is gradually increased to 1500 kN or 1.5 MN. (The multiple can usually be choosen so that the numerical value will be between 0.1 and 1000)

Unit Symbols

Unit symbols are unaltered in the plural:

    1 m,   10 m,   (10 ms means ten milliseconds).

Unit symbols are not followed by a period except at the end of a sentence:

    1 kg   =   1000 g.

Unit symbols are written in lower case unless the unit name is derived from a proper name. Only the first letter is capitalized:

    12 m,   10 kg,   8 V (volt),   6 Pa (pascal).

Where the text is written in upper case letters, symbols are in lower case:

    SPEED LIMIT 50 km / h.

The degree symbol is used with Celsius but not with kelvin:

    25°C   (not 25 °C or 25° C).
    25 C   (coulomb) is a quantity of electricity.
    25 K   not 25°K.

Use of Letter Symbols

The distinction between upper case and lower case symbols is very important. For instance:

K =	kelvin	k =	kilo (10^3)
M =	mega (10^6)	m =	metre (when m is used alone)
		m =	milli (when m is used as a prefix)
N =	newton	n =	nano (10^{-9})
T =	tera	t =	tonne
G =	giga	g =	gram
S =	siemens	s =	second
H =	henry	h =	hour

Decimal Marker

The decimal marker may be a point or a comma. Since both are being used internationally as decimal markers, it is necessary to use spaces to separate long line of digits on either side of the decimal marker:

    1 234.567   NOT   1,234.567
    112 234.567 89   "   112 234.56789

Numerals

When writing a decimal number smaller that one (1), precede the decimal marker with a zero (0):

    0.023   NÒT   .023 or 023

Decimal fractions are preferred to common fractions:

    5.25 rather than 5¼

A dot (·) is used as the multiplication sign for products of units when expressed by symbols:

    N·m   =   Nm

With numerals the multiplication sign ($\times$) is used:

    25 N $\times$ 25 m   =   625 Nm

Exponential Methods of Expressing Numbers.

There are several ways of expressing exponents in the SI, examples are:

Positive notation – multiples of ten

$$10^3 = 10 \times 10 \times 10 = 1000 = kilo = E+03$$

Negative notation – submultiples of ten

$$10^{-3} = \frac{1}{10 \times 10 \times 10} = 1/1000 = milli = E-03$$

Examples of application:

500 000 Pa may be expressed as: 5×10^5 Pa or $5 \times E+05$
500 kPa or 0.5 MPa

0.000 05 Pa may be expressed as: 5×10^{-5} Pa or $5 \times E-05$ Pa
0.05 mPa or 50 μPa

Indices:

In calculations involving indices, the following rules apply:
When multiplying powers of the same number together, add the indices

e.g. $10^2 \times 10^3 = 10^{2+3} = 10^5$
(i.e. $10 \times 10 \times 10 \times 10 \times 10 = 100\ 000 = 10^5$)

When dividing power of the same number, subtract the indices:

e.g. $10^4 \div 10^2 = 10^{4-2} = 10^2$
(i.e. $10\ 000 \div 100 = 100 = 10^2$)

Negative Indices:

e.g. $10^2 \div 10^3 = 10^{2-3} = 10^{-1}$
(i.e. $100 \div 1000 = 100/1000 = 1/10$)
10^{-1} is therefore the same as $1/10$

Rule: Any number with a **minus** index means ONE divided by that number

The power "0":

10^0 is another special case. Its meaning becomes clear if we apply the rules as before:

e.g. $10^1 \times 10^{-1} = 10^{1-1} = 10^0$
(i.e. $10 \times 1/10 = 1$)
10^0 is therefore the same as 1

Rule: Any number of the power "0" equals 1

The use of indices in calculations is especially useful in avoiding mixed multiples of units and awkward decimal quantities. Example:

$$\frac{4 \times 10^3 \text{ kg}}{550 \times 10^{-3} \text{ kg}} \quad \text{NOT} \quad \frac{4 \text{ tonnes}}{550 \text{ g}}$$

Calculations can be simplified by reducing all units to SI units. Example:

$$\frac{6 \times 10^9 \text{ J}}{2 \times 10^{-6} \text{ s}} = 3 \times 10^{15} \text{ J/s} = 3 \text{ PJ/s} = 3 \text{ PW}$$

Errors in calculations can be avoided more easily if prefixes are replaced by power of ten.

$$1 \text{ mg·cm}^2/\text{ns} = 10^{-6} \text{ kg} \times 10^{-4} \text{ m}^2 / 10^{-9} \text{ s}$$
$$= 10^{-6} \text{ kg} \times 10^5 \text{ m}^2 / \text{s}$$
$$= 10^{-1} \text{ kg·m}^2 / \text{s}$$

For convenience in writing and manipulation, numbers are often expressed as factors of appropriate powers of 10.
Example:

2 380 000 may be written 2.38×10^6
238   may be written 2.38×10^2
0.000 238 may be written 2.38×10^{-4}

Example of solution:

$$\frac{6\,600\,000 \times 0.002}{13\,200} = \frac{6.6 \times 10^6 \times 2 \times 10^{-3}}{1.32 \times 10^4}$$
$$= \frac{13.2 \times 10^3}{1.32 \times 10^4} = \frac{1.32 \times 10^4}{1.32 \times 10^4} = 1$$

Terminology

There are three cases where the final vowel in the prefix is commonly omitted:

Prefix	Correct	Incorrect
mega	megohm	megaohm
kilo	kilohm	kiloohm
hecto	hectare	hectoare

In all other cases where the unit name begins with a vowel, both vowels are retained and both pronounced.

The Word "Per"

The slash (/) is used as a separator between the numerator and the denominator of a fraction or to express "per". For example:

radian per second squared for, rad / s^2, $\frac{\text{rad}}{\text{s}^2}$, rad·s^{-2}

When names of units are used, division is indicated by the word "per" and not the slash:

Correct: newton per square metre or N / m^2
Incorrect: newton / square metre – newton / m^2 – N / square metre.

Multiples and Submultiples

In practice it is not always convenient to use the base or derived unit as it stands in everyday measurement, particularly when this results in large numbers of digits. In such cases, decimal multiples or submultiples of the unit may be used, as shown in the following table.

There are 16 multiples and submultiples in all, although only those marked with an asterisk (*) are likely to be met with at all frequently. These SI prefixes, as they are called are written immediately before the symbols for the units to which they apply, with no intervening space or punctuation. Examples:

$$\text{mm} \quad \text{millimetre} \quad = \quad 10^{-3}\ \text{m}$$
$$\text{kPa} \quad \text{kilopascal} \quad = \quad 10^{3}\ \text{Pa}$$

From these examples it can be seen that when an exponent is attached to the symbol for a decimal multiple or submultiple, it applies to the latter, and not to the unit symbol.

$$1\ \text{cm}^3 \quad = \quad 1\ (\text{cm})^3 \quad = \quad (10^{-2}\ \text{m})^3 \quad = \quad 10^{-6}\ \text{m}^3$$

Compound prefixes should not be used. Example: Mm (megametre) not kkm (kilokilometre).

SI PREFIXES

Prefix	Symbol	Factor		Magnitude [1]
exa	E	10^{18}	=	one trillion (M.M.M)
peta	P	10^{15}		
tera	T	10^{12}	=	one billion (M.M)
giga	G	10^{9}		
* mega	M	10^{6}	=	one million (M)
* kilo	k	10^{3}	=	one thousand
hecto	h	10^{2}	=	one hundred
deca	da	10^{1}	=	ten
deci	d	10^{-1}	=	one tenth
* centi	c	10^{-2}	=	one hundredth
* milli	m	10^{-3}	=	one thousandth
* micro	μ	10^{-6}	=	one millionth (1 / M)
nano	n	10^{-9}		
pico	p	10^{-12}	=	one billionth (1 / M.M)
femto	f	10^{-15}		
atto	a	10^{-18}	=	one trillionth (1 / M.M.M)

[1] In 1948, the International Bureau of Weights and Measures has given large numbers the following numerical values. One million (10^6), one billion (10^{12}), one trillion (10^{18}), one quadrillion (10^{24}), one quintillion (10^{30}), ...one centillion (10^{600}).
The British term "milliard" often erroneously called "billion" is one thousand millions (1000 × 1 000 000 or 10^9).
In the United States, the term "billion" means one thousand millions. In most countries the term "billion" means one million millions. Consequently, the term is confusing and should be avoided particularly in technical writing.

– A –

abampere (aA)
Unit of electric current
= 10	A
= 1	cgs emu of current
= 3×10^{10}	cgs esu of current
= 3×10^{10}	sA

abampere per centimetre (aA / cm)
Unit of electric current density
= 1000	A / m
= 1	cgs emu of surface charge density
= 3×10^{10}	sA / cm

abampere per square centimetre (aA / cm²)
Unit of current density
= 5.067×10^{-5}	A / circ. mil
= 6.452×10^{-5}	A / sq. mil
= 64.516	A / in²

abampere turn (aAt)
Unit of magnetomotive force
= 10	At
= 12.566	Gb

abcoulomb (aC)
Unit of electric charge
= 0.002 777	A·h
= 10	C
= 1	cgs emu of charge
= 3×10^{10}	cgs esu of charge
= $6.241\ 96 \times 10^{19}$	electronic charges
= 3×10^{10}	sC

abcoulomb per square centimetre (aC / cm²)
Unit of electric charge density
= 1×10^5	C / m²
= 1	cgs emu of polarization and surface charge density
= 3×10^{10}	cgs esu

abfarad (aF)
Unit of electric capacitance
= 1×10^9	F (= 1 GF)
= 8.988×10^{20}	cgs esu or sF

abhenry (aH)
Unit of electric inductance
= 1	cgs of induction
= 1×10^{-9}	H (= 1 nH)
= 1.112×10^{-21}	sH

abmho (–)
Unit of electric conductance (now siemens)
= 1	cgs emu of conductance
= 1×10^9	S (= 1 GS)
= 8.988×10^{20}	cgs esu or statmhos

abohm (aΩ)
Unit of electric resistance

= 1	cgs emu of resistance
= 8.988 × 10^{20}	cgs esu
= 1 × 10^{-9}	ohm (= 1 nanohm)
= 1.112 × 10^{-21}	statohm

abvolt (aV)
Unit of electric potential

= 1 × 10^{-8}	V
= 10	nV
= 3.335 × 10^{-11}	sV or cgs esu
= 1	cgs emu of emf

abvolt per centimetre (aV / cm)
Unit of electric field intensity

= 1	cgs emu
= 3.335 × 10^{-11}	cgs esu or sV / cm
= 2.54 × 10^{-11}	V / mil
= 1 × 10^{-9}	V / mm

acre (−)
Unit of area (CAN, UK, US)

= 40.468 564	a (are)
= 0.404 685 6	ha
= 4	roods (UK)
= 10	sq. chains (surveyor or Gunter's)
= 4.356	sq. chains (engineer or Ramden's)
= 43 560	ft^2
= 4046.856	m^2
= 160	sq. rods or poles or perches

1 acre, Cunningham, Ireland	= 1.2913 acres (UK)
	= 52.25 ares
1 acre, Irish, Ireland	= 1.6198 acres (UK)
	= 65.55 ares
1 acre, Rhynland, Br. Guiana	= 1.0521 acres (UK)
	= 42.60 ares

acre foot (−)
Unit of volume or irrigation

= 43 560	ft^3
= 1233.49	m^3
= 1613.33	yd^3
= 271 325.7	gal (CAN, UK)
= 325 851	gal (US)
= 1 233 447.3	L

acre foot per day (−)
Unit of volume or capacity

= 14.274	dm^3 / s or L / s
= 188.4	gal / min (CAN)
= 226.3	gal / min (US)
= 1886.58	lbH_2O (60°F) / min

acre foot per second (–)
Unit of volume or capacity

= 1.568 16 × 10^8	ft^3 / h
= 9.767 76 × 10^8	gal / h (CAN)
= 1.173 07 × 10^9	gal / h (US)

acre inch (–)
Unit of volume or capacity

= 3630	ft^3
= 102.79	m^3
= 22 611.1	gal (CAN)
= 27 154.3	gal (US)
= 102 787.3	L

ampere (A)
Unit of electric current flow

= 0.1	aA
= 1	cgs unit of current
= 1	C / s
= 3 × 10^9	sA
= 1.257	Gb

ampere-hour (A·h)
Unit of electric charge

= 3600	C
= 0.037 307	faraday

ampere turn (At)
Unit of magnetism and magnetomotive force

= 1.257	cgs unit
= 1.257	cgs emu
= 1.257	Gb
= 3.767 × 10^{10}	cgs esu

ampere per circular mil (A / cmil)
Unit of electric current density

= 197 353	A / cm^2
= 19 735.3	aA / cm^2

ampere per square mil (A / mil^2)
Unit of electric current density

= 15 500.031	aA / cm^2
= 1.550 003 × 10^5	A / cm^2

angstrom unit (Å)
Unit of length

= 1 × 10^{-10}	m
= 1 × 10^{-8}	cm
= 1 × 10^{-7}	mm
= 0.1	nm (nanometre)

are (a)
Unit of area

= 0.01	ha
= 100	m^2
= 1076.391	ft^2
= 0.024 710 54	acre

arpent (arp)
Unit of length

=	180	ft (France)
=	191.835	ft (Québec)
=	58.472	m

arpent squared (arp²)
Unit of area – Québec

=	0.341 88	ha
=	3418.8	m²
=	36 800	ft²
=	0.845	acre

```
              1 arpent squared:

Seychelles   = 1.043  acres (UK)
             = 42.20  ares
Hungary
  (cadastral) = 1.422  acres (UK)
             = 57.546 ares
Belgium      = 4.172  acres (UK)
             = 168.8  ares
```

assay ton (–)
Unit of mass in testing an alloy or ore

=	450.110 45	gr
=	29.166 666	g
=	1.028 823 9	oz (avdp)
=	0.937 729 84	oz (troy)

assay ton per milligram

=	1	ton (avdp) / oz (troy)

astronomical unit (AU)
Unit of length in astronomy

=	$1.495\ 04 \times 10^8$	km
=	1.581×10^{-5}	l·y· (light year)
=	4.848 14	Mpc (megaparsecs)

atmosphere, normal (atm)
Unit of pressure

=	1.013 25	bar
=	760	mmHg (0°C) or torrs
=	1033.23	gf / cm²
=	101.325	kPa
=	101 325	Pa (N / m²)
=	14.696	lbf / in² (psi)
=	10.333	t / m²
=	1.0581	tn / ft²

atmosphere, technical (at)
Unit of pressure

=	98.065	kPa
=	1	kp / cm²
=	735.56	mmHg (0°C)

atomic mass unit (u)
Unit of energy used in atomic physics

$$= 1.6604 \times 10^{-24} \quad \text{g}$$
$$= 1.4923 \times 10^{-10} \quad \text{J}$$
$$= 1.4923 \times 10^{-3} \quad \text{erg}$$
$$= 6.8464 \times 10^{7} \quad \text{Ry (rydberg)}$$
$$= 7.3148 \times 10^{8} \quad \text{eV}$$
$$= 7.5131 \times 10^{12} \quad \text{cm}^{-1} \text{ (reciprocal centimetre)}$$
$$= 1.0810 \times 10^{13} \quad \text{K (kelvin)}$$
$$= 2.2524 \times 10^{23} \quad \text{s}^{-1} \text{ (reciprocal second)}$$

Base units expressed in other units		
$A \cdot s$	=	1 C (coulomb)
$A \cdot s / V$	=	1 F (farad)
$A^2 \cdot s^3 / (kg \cdot m^2)$	=	1 S (siemens)
$A^2 \cdot s^4 / (kg \cdot m^2)$	=	1 F (farad)
A / V	=	1 S (siemens)

– B –

bag (–)
Unit of volume (UK)

= 3	bushels (UK)*
= 3.853 045	ft^3
= 24	gal (UK)

* The abbreviation (bu) is used in US only

bag of cement (–)
Unit of volume and mass (UK)

= 0.25	bbl (cement)
= 1	ft^3
= 94	lb

bar (bar)
Unit of pressure

= 0.986 923	atm
= 1.019 72	at
= 750.06	mmHg or torr (0°C)
= 100 000	Pa (N / m^2)
= 100	kPa
= 10	N / cm^2
= 29.53	inHg (32°F)
= 1 × 10^6	baryes
= 14.5038	lbf / in^2 (psi)
= 10.197	tf / m^2
= 1.0442	tnf / ft^2
= 0.932 385	tonf / ft^2

barn (b)
Unit of cross section for nuclear collisions

= 100	fm^2 (sq. femtometre)
= 10^{-28}	m^2

Supplementary units		
b / eV	= 6.241 × 10^{-10}	m^2 / J
b / erg	= 1 × 10^{-21}	m^2 / J
b / sr	= 1 × 10^{-28}	m^2 / sr
b / (sr.eV)	= 6.241 × 10^{-10}	m^2 / (sr.J)
b / (sr.erg)	= 1 × 10^{-21}	m^2 / (sr.J)

barrel, brewers (bbl)

= 0.717 025	barrel (UK)
= 0.984 126	bbl (US liq.)
= 7161	in^3
= 0.117 348	m^3
= 25.813	gal (UK)
= 31	gal (US)
= 117.348	L

barrel (UK)
The UK or British barrel is the same for both liquid and dry measure.

=	1.5	bags (UK)
=	1.4154 04	bbl (US dry)
=	1.372 513	bbl (US liq.)
=	4.5	bushel (UK)
=	4.644 253	bu (US)
=	0.163 659	m^3
=	36	gal (UK)
=	163.659	dm^3 or L

barrel, beer (UK)

=	36	gal (UK)
=	43.234 17	gal (US liq.)

barrel, cranberry (US)

=	2.709 238	bu (US)
=	5826	in^3
=	86.695 623	qt (US dry)
=	95.471 25	dm^3 or L

barrel, petroleum (US)

=	34.972 32	gal (CAN or UK)
=	42	gal (US)
=	158.987	L
=	0.158 987	m^3

barrel (US dry)

=	0.706 511 85	bbl (UK)
=	0.969 696	bbl (US liq.)
=	3.281 219 5	bu (US)
=	7056	in^3
=	115.627 12	dm^3 or L

barrel (US liq.)
In the US the liquid barrel varies from 31 to 42 gallons.

=	0.728 590	bbl (UK)
=	1.031 25	bbl (US dry)
=	1	bbl (wine)
=	7276.5	in^3
=	0.119 240 5	m^3
=	26.229 25	gal (UK)
=	31.5	gal (US liq.)
=	119.2405	L

barrel of cement (–)

=	4	bags of cement
=	376	lb
=	170.6	kg

Supplementary units			
bbl / d	=	1.84	cm^3 / s
bbl / (d·lbf·in²)	=	0.023	m^3 / (d·kPa)
bbl / ft	=	0.521 61	m^3 / m
bbl / h	=	44.163	cm^3 / s or mL / s
bbl / (M·ft³)	=	0.133	dm^3 / kmol
bbl / tn	=	175.253	dm^3 / t
bbl / ton	=	156.476	dm^3 / t

barye (−)
Unit of pressure

=	1×10^{-6}	bar
=	1	dyn / cm²
=	$1.019\ 72 \times 10^{-3}$	g / cm²
=	0.001	millibar

blondel (−)
Unit of luminance

=	1	asb (apostilb)
=	0.1	mLa (millilambert)

board foot (−)
The contents of a board 1 ft² × 1 in

=	144	in³
=	2359.7	cm³ (30.48 × 30.48 × 2.54) cm

British thermal unit (Btu)
Unit of energy

=	1055.06	J or N·m
=	3.930×10^{-4}	hp·h
=	778.179	ft·lbf
=	0.252	kcal
=	0.2928	W·h

Btu per cubic foot (Btu / ft³)
Unit of calorific value (volume basis)

=	37.2589	mJ / cm³ or kJ / m³
=	8.9	kcal / m³
=	$1.605\ 44 \times 10^{-6}$	therm / gal (UK)
=	$8.902\ 16 \times 10^{-6}$	th / L

Btu per cubic foot °F [Btu / (ft³·°F)]
Unit of specific heat capacity (volume basis)

=	67.066	mJ / (cm³·°C)
=	67.066	kJ / (m³·°C)
=	16.0185	kcal / (m³·°C)

Btu per foot hour °F [Btu / (ft·h·°F)]
Unit of thermal conductivity

=	17.307	mW / (cm·K)
=	0.017 307	W / (cm·K)
=	1.488 16	kcal / (m·h·°C)

Btu per (CAN) gallon (Btu / gal)
Unit of calorific value

=	232.0798	kJ / m³
=	0.232 079 8	MJ / m³

Btu per (US) gallon (Btu / gal)
Unit of calorific value

=	278.7163	kJ / m³
=	0.278 716 3	MJ / m³

Btu per hour (Btu / h)
Unit of power

= 2 928 700	erg / s
= 12.961	ft·lbf / min
= 0.292 87	W (absolute)
= 0.292 83	W (Int)
= 0.016 666	Btu / min
= 4.2 × 10^{-3}	kg·cal / min
= 3.9819 × 10^{-4}	hp (metric)
= 3.9275 × 10^{-4}	hp
= 3.9259 × 10^{-4}	hp (electric)
= 2.9287 × 10^{-4}	kW (abs)
= 2.9282 × 10^{-4}	kW (Int)
= 2.7778 × 10^{-4}	Btu / s

Btu per hour (Btu / h)
Unit of power (energy flow rate)

= 0.293 071	W
= 0.07	cal / s
= 0.251 996	kcal / h

BTU per minute (Btu / min)
Unit of power or energy

= 1.757 × 10^8	erg / s
= 17.572	W (abs)
= 17.569	W (Int)
= 12.96	ft·lbf / s
= 0.2519	kg·cal / min
= 2.389 × 10^{-2}	hp (metric)
= 1.757 × 10^{-2}	kW (abs)
= 1.756 × 10^{-2}	kW (Int)
= 1.667 × 10^{-2}	Btu / s

Btu per pound (Btu / lb)
Unit of calorific value (mass basis)

= 2.326	J / g or kJ / kg
= 0.555 56	kcal / kg
= 778.169	ft·lbf / lb
= 237.186	kgf·m / kg
= 2326	J / kg

Btu per pound °F [Btu / (lb·°F)]
Unit of specific heat capacity

= 4.1868	J / (g·K)
= 1	kcal / (kg·°C)
= 778.169	ft·lbf / (lb·°F)

Btu per second (Btu / s)
Unit of power

= 1054.3	W (abs)
= 252	g·cal / s
= 15.12	kg·cal / min
= 1.433	hp (metric)
= 1.414	hp
= 1.413	hp (electric)
= 777.8	ft·lbf / s

Btu per square foot hour [Btu / (ft^2·h)]
Unit of intensity of heat flow rate
$\quad$ = 3.154 59 × 10^{-4} $\qquad$ W / cm^2
$\quad$ = 3.154 59 $\qquad$ W / m^2
$\quad$ = 2.712 46 $\qquad$ kcal / (m^2·h)

Btu per square foot hour °F [Btu / (ft^2·h·°F)]
Unit of thermal conductance
$\quad$ = 5.678 26 × 10^{-4} $\qquad$ W / (cm^2·K)
$\quad$ = 5.678 26 $\qquad$ W / (m^2·K)
$\quad$ = 4.882 43 $\qquad$ kcal / (m^2·h·°C)

Btu inch per square foot hour °F [Btu·in / (ft^2·h·°F)]
Unit of thermal conductivity
$\quad$ = 1.442 28 × 10^{-3} $\qquad$ W / (cm·K)
$\quad$ = 3.444 82 × 10^{-4} $\qquad$ cal / (cm·s·°C)
$\quad$ = 0.124 014 $\qquad$ kcal / (m·h·°C)
$\quad$ = 0.083 333 $\qquad$ Btu / (ft·h·°F)

Btu per short ton (Btu / tn)
Unit of calorific value
$\quad$ = 1.163 $\qquad$ kJ / t

bushel (UK bu)
Unit of volume
$\quad$ = 1.032 050 $\qquad$ bu (US)
$\quad$ = 1.284 35 $\qquad$ ft^3
$\quad$ = 8 $\qquad$ gal (UK)
$\quad$ = 36.368 74 $\qquad$ dm^3

bushel (US bu)
Unit of volume (dry measure)
$\quad$ = 0.968 939 $\qquad$ bu (UK)
$\quad$ = 0.304 764 $\qquad$ bbl (US dry)
$\quad$ = 1.244 $\qquad$ ft^3
$\quad$ = 9.309 177 $\qquad$ gal (US liq.)
$\quad$ = 35.238 $\qquad$ dm^3 or L
$\quad$ = 4 $\qquad$ pecks
$\quad$ = 32 $\qquad$ qt (US dry)

bushel per acre (−)
Unit of density or concentration
$\quad$ = 89.89 $\qquad$ dm^3 / ha (UK)
$\quad$ = 87.075 $\qquad$ dm^3 / ha (US)

butt (−)
UK unit of volume and capacity
$\quad$ = 126 $\qquad$ gal (UK)
$\quad$ = 572.7 $\qquad$ L

– C –

calorie (cal)
Unit of energy and power

=	4.186×10^7	erg
=	3.087	lbf
=	99.336	ft·pdl
=	4.1868	$J_{(IT)}$
=	4.184	$J_{(tc)}$

Supplementary units		
1 cal (dietetic)	=	4.1855 kJ
1 cal $_{(IT)}$ / g	=	4186.8 J / kg
1 cal $_{(IT)}$ / (g·°C)	=	4186.8 J / (kg.·K)
1 cal $_{(IT)}$ / (g·K)	=	4186.8 J / (kg·K)
1 cal / (s·cm·°C)	=	418.68 W / (m·K)
1 cal / (s·m²·°C)	=	418.68 W / (m²·K)
1 cal / mL	=	4.1840 kJ / kg
1 cal / lb	=	9.2250 J / kg

calorie per second (cal / s)
Unit of power (energy flow rate)

=	4.1868	W
=	3.6	kcal / h
=	14.286	Btu / h

calorie per centimetre second °C [cal / (cm·s·°C)]
Unit of thermal conductivity

=	4.1868	W / (cm·K)
=	360	kcal / (m·h·°C)
=	241.1	Btu / (ft·h·°F)
=	2902.91	Btu·in / (ft²·h·°F)

calorie per square centimetre second [cal / (cm²·s)]
Unit of intensity of heat flow rate

=	4.1868	W / cm²
=	36 000	kcal / (m²·h)
=	13 272.1	Btu / (ft²·h)
=	1	langley / s

calorie per square centimetre second °C [cal / (cm²·s·°C)]

=	4.1868	W / (cm²·K)
=	36 000	kcal / (m²·h·°C)
=	7373.38	Btu / (ft²·h·°F)

candela (cd)
Base unit of luminous intensity
    = 1   lm / sr

Supplementary units		
1 cd	= 1	candle (Int)
1 cd / cm^2	= 1	stilb
1 cd / ft^2	= 10.77	cd / m^2
1 cd / in^2	= 1550	cd / m^2
1 cd / m^2	= 0.093	cd / ft^2
"	= 0.29186	ft lambert
"	= 1	lm / (sr·m^2)
"	= 1	nit
"	= 6.45 × 10^{-4}	cd / in^2
"	= 3.14 × 10^{-4}	lambert
1 cd·sr	= 1	lumen

candle power spherical (–)
Unit of luminous flux
    = 12.566 370   lm (lumen)

carat (–)
Parts of gold per 24 of mixture
    = 41.666   mg / g

carat (metric)
Unit of mass
    = 3.086 47   gr
    = 0.2   g
    = 200   mg

cental (ctl)
Unit of mass
    = 45.369 237   kg
    = 100   lb

centigrade heat units (CHU)
Unit of energy and power
    = 1.8   Btu
    = 453.6   cal
    = 1897.52   J
    = 0.527 088   W·h

centigram (cg)
Unit of mass
    = 0.154 323 6   gr
    = 0.01   g

centilitre (cL)
Unit of capacity
    = 10   cm^3
    = 0.610 255   in^3
    = 2.705 198   dr (US fl)
    = 0.338 15   oz (US fl)

centimetre (cm^{-1}) or reciprocal centimetre
energy used in atomic physics
=	2.2101×10^{-37}	g
=	1.9863×10^{-23}	J
=	1.9863×10^{-16}	erg
=	1.3310×10^{-13}	u (atomic mass unit)
=	9.1127×10^{-6}	Ry (rydberg)
=	1.2398×10^{-4}	eV
=	1.4388	K (kelvin)
=	2.9980×10^{10}	s^{-1} (reciprocal second)

centimetre (cm)
Unit of length
=	10	mm
=	1×10^{-8}	Å (angstrom)
=	0.3937	in
=	0.032 808	ft
=	0.010 936	yd
=	0.049 709	link (surveyor or Gunter's)
=	0.032 808	link (engineer or Ramden's)

centimetre of mercury (cmHg, 0°C)
Unit of pressure
=	0.013 157 805	atm
=	0.013 332	bar
=	13 332.2	dyn / cm^2
=	10	torr
=	1333.2	Pa
=	0.193 37	lbf / in^2 (psi)

centimetre of water (cmH$_2$0, 4°C)
Unit of pressure
=	98.063	Pa
=	0.014 223	lbf / in^2 (psi)
=	1	g / cm^2

centimetre per second (cm / s)
Unit of velocity
=	1.968 504	ft / min
=	0.6	m / min
=	0.036	km / h
=	6×10^{-4}	km / min
=	1×10^{-5}	km / s

centimetre per second squared (cm / s^2)
Unit of acceleration
=	0.036	km / (h·s)
=	0.022 369	mi / (h·s)
=	2.0885	lbf·s / ft^2

centipoise (cP)
Unit of dynamic viscosity
=	0.01	g / (cm·s)
=	1	mN·s / m^2 or mPa·s
=	0.001	Pa·s
=	2.088×10^{-5}	lb·s / ft^2

centistokes (cSt)
Unit of kinematic viscosity
=	1	mm^2 / s
=	0.038 750	ft^2 / h

chain, surveyor or Gunter's (ch)
Unit of length
=	2011.68	cm
=	792	in
=	100	li (link)
=	66	ft
=	0.1	furlong
=	20.1168	m

chain, engineer or Ramden's (ch)
Unit of length
=	3048.006	cm
=	1200	in
=	100	li (link)
=	100	ft
=	0.151	furlong
=	30.48	m

circle or revolution (...^{r})
Unit of angular measure
=	1 296 000	..." (second)
=	21 600	...' (minute)
=	400	...^{g} (grade)
=	360	...^{o} (degree)
=	6.283 185	rad (radian)
=	4	...^{L} (quadrant or right angle)

circular inch (cin)
Unit of area
=	645.16	circ. mm
=	5.067 075	cm^2
=	0.785 398	in^2

circular mil (cmil)
Unit of area
=	507	μm^2 (sq. micrometre)
=	0.785 398	mil^2

circular millimetre (circ. mm)
Unit of area
=	1550.003	circ. mils
=	1 217.37	sq. mils
=	0.785 396	mm^2
=	0.001 217 37	in^2
=	0.001 550 003	circ. in

coulomb (C)
Unit of electric charge

= 1	A·s
= 0.1	aC (abcoulomb)
= 3 × 10^9	sC
= 6.243 × 10^{18}	electronic charges
= 2.777 78 × 10^{-4}	A·h
= 12.566 371	cgs unit of displacement flux
= 1	cgs unit of electric charge
= 1.256 637	cgs emu of displacement flux
= 0.1	cgs emu of electric charge
= 3.767 31 × 10^{10}	cgs esu of displacement flux
= 2.997 93 × 10^9	cgs esu of electric charge

coulomb per cubic metre (C / m³)
Unit of electric charge per volume

= 1 × 10^{-7}	aC / cm³
= 1 × 10^{-6}	cgs unit of volume charge density
= 1 × 10^{-6}	C / cm³
= 1 × 10^{-7}	cgs emu of volume charge density
= 2997.93	cgs esu or sC / cm³

coulomb per kilogram (C / kg)
Unit of electric charge per mass

= 1.019 716 × 10^{-6}	C / dyn
= 0.453 592 27	C / lb
= 3057.04	sC / dyn

coulomb per square metre (C / m²)
Unit of electric charge per area

= 0.0001	cgs unit of polarization and surface charge density
= 1.256 637 × 10^{-4}	cgs emu of displacement
= 1 × 10^{-5}	cgs emu of polarization and surface charge density
= 299 793.0	cgs esu of polarization and surface charge density
= 299 793.0	sC / cm²

cran (UK)
Unit of volume (fishing industry)

= 6.020 384	ft³
= 37.5	gal (UK)
= 170.474	L

cubic centimetre (cm³)
Unit of volume (same as mL)

= 0.001	dm³ or L
= 1 × 10^{-6}	m³ or kL
= 0.061 023 744	in³
= 1000	mm³
= 16.893 65	minims (UK)
= 16.230 66	minims (US)
= 0.035 195	oz (UK fl)
= 0.033 814	oz (US fl)

cubic centimetre per cubic metre (cm³ / m³)
Unit of concentration
= 0.034 972	gal (CAN) / 1000 bbl
= 0.042	gal (US) / 1000 bbl

cubic centimetre per second (cm³ / s)
Unit of flow rate
= 0.06	L / min
= 0.022 643	bbl / h (petroleum)
= 0.013 21	gal / min (CAN)
= 0.015 85	gal / min (US)
= 0.002 119	ft³ / min
= 0.001	L / s
= $2.199\ 69 \times 10^{-4}$	gal / s (CAN)
= $2.641\ 72 \times 10^{-4}$	gal / s (US)

cubic centimetre atmosphere (cm³·atm)
Unit of energy
= 9.61×10^{-5}	Btu
= 0.101 325	J
= 2.814×10^{-5}	W·h

cubic centimetre atmosphere per gram (cm³·atm / g)
Unit of thermal capacity
= 0.043 591	Btu / lb
= 33.899	ft·lbf / lb
= 0.101 325	J / g
= $2.814\ 56 \times 10^{-8}$	W·h / h

cubic decimetre (dm³)
Unit of volume (same as litre)
= 1000	cm³ or mL
= 61.023 68	in³
= 0.219 969	gal (CAN)
= 0.264 172	gal (US)
= 1.759 76	pt (CAN)
= 2.113 38	pt (US)

cubic decimetre per cubic metre (dm³ / m³)
Unit of volume per unit of volume
= 7.758 40	bbl / acre ft
= 1	cm³ / dm³
= 0.996	oz (UK fl) / ft³
= 0.958	oz (US fl) / ft³

cubic decimetre per kilogram (dm³ / kg)
Unit of volume per unit mass
= 1	cm³ / g or mm³ / mg
= 1	m³ / Mg or kL / t
= 0.099 776	gal (UK) / lb
= 0.119 826	gal (US) / lb

cubic decimetre per mole (dm³ / mol)
Unit of volume per unit mole
= 7.518 232	bbl / Mft³ (60°F)
= 0.263 138	gal (UK) / 1000 ft³ (60°F)
= 0.315 765	gal (US) / 1000 ft³ (60°F)

cubic decimetre per second (dm³ / s)
Unit volume per time or flow rate

= 13.198 15	gal (UK) / min
= 15.850 32	gal (US) / min

cubic decimetre per tonne (dm³ / t)
Unit of volume per unit of volume

= 0.223 493	gal (UK) / ton
= 0.199 613	gal (UK) / tn
= 0.268 411	gal (US) / ton
= 0.239 653	gal (US) / tn

cubic foot (ft³)
Unit of volume

= 12	board ft
= 0.778 605	bushel (UK)
= 0.803 564	bu (US)
= 1728	in³
= 0.028 316 85	m³
= 0.037 037	yd³
= 6.228 84	gal (UK)
= 7.480 52	gal (US)
= 6.428 52	gal (US dry)
= 28.316 85	L
= 996.614	oz (UK fl)
= 957.507	oz (US fl)
= 0.01	ton (register)

cubic foot per hour (ft³ / h)
Unit of volume per time or flow rate

= 7.865 79	cm³ / s or mL / s
= 679.585	dm³ / d or L / d
= 471.934	cm³ / min or mL / min

cubic foot per minute (ft³ / min)
Unit of volume per time or flow rate

= 0.033 057 851	acre ft / d
= 471.947 44	cm³ / s
= 6.2288	gal (UK) / min
= 7.480 519 5	gal (US) / min
= 0.472	L / s
= 10.686	bbl (42 US gal) / h
= 28.316 85	dm³ / min or L / min
= 1.7	m³ / h

cubic foot per second (ft³ / s)
Unit of volume per time or flow rate

= 101.941	m³ / h
= 1699	L / min
= 641.18	bbl (42 US gal) / h
= 28 316.8	cm³ / s

	Supplementary units		
$ft^3 / (min \cdot ft^2)$	=	0.0058	$m^3 / (s \cdot m^2)$ or m / s
ft^3 / lb	=	62.427 96	cm^3 / g
$ft^3 / (lb \cdot in^2)$	=	195.3	J
$ft^3 \cdot atm$	=	2.7213	Btu
"	=	2868.74	J
$ft^3 H_2 0$	=	62.426	$lbH_2 0$ (39.2°F)
$ft^3 H_2 0 / h$	=	1496.8	$lbH_2 0 / d$
"	=	62.365	$lbH_2 0 / h$ (60°F)
"	=	0.668 85	$tonH_2 0 / d$
"	=	0.7484	$tnH_2 0 / d$
"	=	0.679 78	$tH_2 0 / d$

cubic hectometre (hm³)
Unit of volume

=	0.001	km^3
=	1×10^6	m^3

cubic inch (in³)
Unit of volume

=	16.387 07	cm^3 or mL
=	6.944×10^{-3}	board ft
=	1.638 661	cL
=	16 387.064	mm^3
=	0.576 744	oz (UK fl)
=	0.554 112 55	oz (US fl)

cubic kilometre (km³)
Unit of volume

=	810.713	acre ft
=	1000	hm^3
=	1×10^9	m^3
=	2.1997×10^{11}	gal (UK)
=	2.6417×10^{11}	gal (US)

cubic metre (m³)
Unit of volume

=	8.1071×10^{-4}	acre ft
=	6.110 261	bbl (UK)
=	6.2898	bbl (petroleum)
=	8.386 415	bbl (US liq.)
=	6.648 49	bbl (US dry)
=	27.496 17	bushel (UK)
=	28.377 59	bu (US)
=	35.314 67	ft^3
=	1.3079	yd^3
=	219.9694	gal (UK)
=	264.1721	gal (US)
=	1	kilolitre
=	1	stère
=	1	tonne

Supplementary units		
$m^3 / (d \cdot kPa)$	= 43.366	$bbl / (d \cdot lbf \cdot in^2)$
m^3 / g	= 16 018.46	ft^3 / lb
m^3 / h	= 0.061 103	gal (UK) / s
"	= 0.073 381	gal (US) / s
m^3 / kg	= 16.018 46	ft^3 / lb
m^3 / m	= 1.917 34	bbl / ft
"	= 0.159 761	bbl / in
"	= 10.763 91	ft^3 / ft
"	= 67.049	gal (UK) / ft
"	= 80.519 64	gal (US) / ft

cubic metre per minute (m^3 / min)
Unit of volume flow rate

= 1.167 427	acre ft / d
= 3.666 156	gal (UK) / s
= 4.402 876	gal (US) / s
= 60 000	L / h
= 1000	L / min
= 16.667	L / s

cubic metre per second (m^3 / s)
Unit of volume flow rate

= 3 600 000	dm^3 / h
= 60 000	dm^3 / min
= 2118.88	ft^3 / min
= 35.314 66	ft^3 / s
= 78.447	yd^3 / min

cubic metre per second metre $[m^3 / (s \cdot m)] = (m^2 / s)$
Unit of flow rate per length (volume basis)

= 241 367.8	gal (UK) / (h·ft)
= 289 870.7	gal (US) / (h·ft)
= 20 113.98	gal (UK) / (h·in)
= 24 155.9	gal (US) / (h·in)
= 4022.796	gal (UK) / (min·ft)
= 4831.879	gal (US) / (min·ft)

cubic metre per second square metre $[m^3 / (s \cdot m^2)] = (m / s)$
Unit of flow rate per area (volume basis)

= 3.280 84	$ft^3 / (s \cdot ft^2)$
= 196.8504	$ft^3 / (min \cdot ft^2)$
= 73 571.96	gal (UK) / (h·ft²)
= 88 352.57	gal (US) / (h·ft²)
= 510.895	gal (UK) / (h·in²)
= 613.5598	gal (US) / (h·in²)
= 1226.148	gal (UK) / (min·ft²)
= 1472.543	gal (US) / (min·ft²)

cubic metre per tonne (m^3 / t)
Unit of volume per mass

= 6.390 744	bbl / ton
= 5.706 020	bbl / tn

cubic yard (yd³)
Unit of volume

=	764.555	dm³ or L
=	27	ft³
=	46 656	in³
=	168.18	gal (UK)
=	201.974	gal (US)
=	173.57	gal (US dry)

cubic yard per minute (yd³ / min)
Unit of volume per time

=	288.534	bbl / h
=	0.45	ft³ / s
=	168.179	gal (UK) / min
=	201.974	gal (US) / min
=	764.55	dm³ / min or L / min

	Miscellaneous units		
cubit	=	45.72	cm
cunit	=	100	ft³
"	=	2.831 68	m³
curie (Ci)	=	3.7×10^{10}	s⁻¹ or 1 / s
"	=	37	GBq
Ci / g	=	3.7×10^{13}	Bq / kg (s⁻¹·kg⁻¹)
cut (woolen yarn)	=	0.001 652 33	kg / m
"	=	605.216	m / kg
"	=	0.003 333	lb / yd
"	=	300	yd / lb

– D –

darcy (D)
Unit of permeability of rock layers

= 1 × 10⁻¹²	m²	
= 1 ~~0.987 exactly~~	μm²	

$= 1 \times 10^{-12}$ m²
$= 1$ μm²   0.987 exactly

day (d)
Unit of mean solar time

= 24	h	(mean solar)
= 1440	min	" "
= 86 400	s	" "
= 0.142 857 14	week	(mean calendar)
= 0.032 876 12	month	" "
= 0.002 739 73	year	(calendar)

day (30) per month
Unit of mean solar time

= 2 592 000	s	
= 43 200	min	
= 720	h	
= 30	d	
= 4.285 714	wk	
= 0.967 742	31 d / month	
= 0.082 192	yr	

day (31) per month
Unit of mean solar time

= 2 678 400	s	
= 44 640	min	
= 744	h	
= 31	d	
= 4.428 571	wk	
= 1.033 333	30 d / month	
= 0.084 932	yr	

degree (...°)
Unit of angular measure

= 1.111	...ᵍ	(grade)
= 60	...′	(minute)
= 3600	...″	(second)
= 0.011 111	...ᴸ	(quadrant)
= 0.002 777	...ʳ	(revolution)
= 0.017 453 293	rad	(radian)

Supplementary units			
1 ...° / ft	=	5.726 145 × 10⁻⁴	rad / cm
1 ...° / in	=	6.871 360 × 10⁻³	rad / cm
1 ...° / min	=	2.908 882 × 10⁻⁴	rad / cm
"	=	4.629 630 × 10⁻⁵	...ʳ / s
1 ...° / s	=	0.017 453	rad / s
"	=	0.166 666	...ʳ / min
"	=	2.777 778 × 10⁻³	...ʳ / s
"	=	1.111 111	...ᵍ / s
1 ...° / h	=	2.777 777 × 10⁻⁴	...° / s
"	=	3.086 419 × 10⁻⁴	...ᵍ / s
"	=	4.848 137 × 10⁻⁶	rad / s
"	=	7.716 049 × 10⁻⁷	...ʳ / s

drachm, fluid (UK dr)
Unit of volume (apoth. or troy)

=	3.551 63	cm^3 or mL
=	0.960 75	dr (US)
=	60	minims
=	0.125	oz fl

dram, fluid (US dr)
Unit of volume (apoth. or troy)

=	3.6967	cm^3 or mL
=	1.040 85	dr (UK)
=	60	minims
=	0.125	oz fl

dram (avdp dr)
Unit of mass

=	1771.8	mg
=	27.34	gr
=	1.7718	g
=	1.367	sc (apoth.)
=	0.456	dr (apoth.)
=	0.0625	oz (avdp)
=	0.0569	oz (apoth.)

dram (apoth. or troy dr)
Unit of mass

=	3887.9	mg
=	60	gr
=	3.888	g
=	0.1372	oz (avdp)
=	0.125	oz (troy)

dyne (dyn)
Unit of force

=	1×10^{-5}	N
=	10	μN
=	1	$g \cdot cm / s^2$
=	1.0197×10^{-6}	kgf
=	1.0197×10^{-9}	tf

Supplementary units			
dyn / (Bi·cm)	=	1×10^{-4}	T
dyn / Bi^2	=	$1.256\ 64 \times 10^{-6}$	H / m
dyn / cm	=	1	erg / cm^2
"	=	0.001	N / m
dyn / cm^2	=	1×10^{-6}	bar
"	=	1	barye
"	=	0.1	N / m^2 or Pa
dyn / cm^3	=	10	N / m^3
dyn / Fr	=	29 979.0	V / m
dyn·cm	=	1	erg
"	=	1×10^{-7}	J or N·m
dyn·cm / Bi	=	1×10^{-8}	Wb
dyn·s	=	1×10^{-5}	kg·m / s
dyn·s / cm	=	10	N·s / m

– E –

electromagnetic unit (emu)
Unit of magnetic flux
= 1	Mx	(maxwell)
= 1×10^{-8}	Wb	(weber)

electromagnetic unit (emu)
Unit of magnetic flux density
= 1	Gs	(gauss)
= 1	Mx / cm^2	
= 1×10^{-8}	Wb / cm^2	

electromagnetic unit (emu)
Unit of magnetomotive force
= 1	Gb	(gilbert)

Supplementary units		
1 emu of capacitance	= 1	GF
1 emu of current	= 10	A
1 emu of potential	= 1×10^{-8}	V
1 emu of inductance	= 1	nH

electronvolt (eV)
Unit of energy
= $1.602\ 19 \times 10^{-19}$	J	
= $1.073\ 56 \times 10^{-9}$	amu	
= $1.181\ 65 \times 10^{-12}$	erg	
= $1.181\ 65 \times 10^{-19}$	ft·lbf	
= $3.829\ 11 \times 10^{-20}$	g·cal	

Supplementary units		
eV / cm	= $1.602\ 19 \times 10^{-17}$	J / m
eV / (cm^2·s)	= $1.602\ 19 \times 10^{-15}$	W / m^2
eV·cm^2	= $1.602\ 19 \times 10^{-15}$	J·m^2
eV·cm^2 / g	= $1.602\ 19 \times 10^{-20}$	J·m^2 / kg

electronvolt (eV)
Unit of energy used in atomic physics
= 1.7826×10^{-33}	g	(gram)
= 1.6021×10^{-19}	J	(joule)
= 1.6021×10^{-12}	erg	(erg)
= 1.0736×10^{-9}	u	(atomic mass unit)
= 7.3500×10^{-2}	Ry	(rydberg)
= 8.0657×10^{3}	cm^{-1}	(reciprocal centimetre)
= 1.1605×10^{4}	K	(kelvin)
= 2.4180×10^{14}	s^{-1}	(reciprocal second)

electrostatic unit (esu)
Unit of magnetism and magnetic flux
= 3×10^{10}	Mx	(maxwell)
= 300	Wb	(weber)

electrostatic unit (esu)
Unit of magnetism and magnetic flux density
= 3×10^{10}	Gs	(gauss)
= 3×10^{6}	T	(tesla)

electrostatic unit (esu)
Unit of magnetism and magnetomotive force
$$= 3.336 \times 10^{-11} \quad \text{Gb} \quad \text{(gilbert)}$$
$$= 2.654 \times 10^{-11} \quad \text{At} \quad \text{(ampere turn)}$$

electrostatic unit (esu)
Unit of magnetism and magnetic flux density
$$= 2.654 \times 10^{-9} \quad \text{At / m}$$
$$= 2.654 \times 10^{-11} \quad \text{At / cm}$$
$$= 3.335 \times 10^{-11} \quad \text{Oe} \quad \text{(oersted)}$$

Supplementary units		
1 esu of capacitance	= 1.113	pF
1 esu of current	= 0.333 560	nA
1 esu of potential	= 300	V
1 esu of inductance	= 8.9875×10^{11}	H
1 esu of resistance	= 8.9875×10^{11}	Ω
"	= 89.8755	T

erg (erg)
Unit of energy and power
$$= 1 \times 10^{-7} \quad \text{J}$$

erg (erg)
Unit of energy used in atomic physics
$$= 1.1126 \times 10^{-21} \quad \text{g} \quad \text{(gram)}$$
$$= 1.0 \quad \times 10^{-7} \quad \text{J} \quad \text{(joule)}$$
$$= 6.7011 \times 10^{2} \quad \text{u} \quad \text{(atomic mass unit)}$$
$$= 4.5878 \times 10^{10} \quad \text{Ry} \quad \text{(rydberg)}$$
$$= 6.2418 \times 10^{11} \quad \text{eV} \quad \text{(electronvolt)}$$
$$= 5.0345 \times 10^{15} \quad \text{cm}^{-1} \quad \text{(reciprocal centimetre)}$$
$$= 7.2435 \times 10^{15} \quad \text{K} \quad \text{(kelvin)}$$
$$= 1.5093 \times 10^{26} \quad \text{s}^{-1} \quad \text{(reciprocal second)}$$

Supplementary units			
erg / bi^2	=	1×10^{-9}	H
erg / cm	=	1×10^{-5}	J / m
erg / (cm·s·°C)	=	1×10^{-5}	W / (m·K)
erg / cm^3	=	0.1	J / m^3
erg / (cm^3·°C)	=	0.1	J / (m^3·K)
erg / (cm^3·nm)	=	1×10^8	J / m^4
erg / (cm^3·s)	=	0.1	W / m^3
erg / Fr	=	300	V
erg / g	=	1×10^{-4}	J / kg
erg / (g·°C)	=	1×10^{-4}	J / (kg·K)
erg / (g·s)	=	1×10^{-4}	W / kg
erg / s	=	1×10^{-7}	W
erg / (s·cm^2)	=	1×10^{-3}	W / m^2
erg / (s·sr)	=	1×10^{-7}	W / sr
erg / (s·sr·cm^2)	=	1×10^{-3}	W / (sr·m^2)
erg / cm^2	=	1×10^{-3}	N / m
erg / (cm^2·s)	=	1×10^{-3}	W / m^2
erg / (cm^2·s·°C)	=	1×10^{-3}	W / (m^2·K)
erg / (cm^2·s·K^4)	=	1×10^{-3}	W / (m^2·K^4)
erg·s	=	1×10^{-7}	J·s
erg·cm^2	=	1×10^{-11}	J / m^2
erg·cm^2 / g	=	1×10^{-8}	J·m^2 / kg
erg·cm^2 / s	=	1×10^{-11}	W·m^2

– F –

farad (F)
Unit of capacitance

= 1	C / V
= 1	A·s / V
= 1	$m^{-2} \cdot kg^{-1} \cdot s^4 \cdot A^2$
= 1 × 10^{-9}	aF (abfarad)
= 1	cgs esu of capacitance

faraday (chemical)
Unit of charge

= 9649.57	aC
= 26.804	A·h
= 96.496	kC

faraday (physical)
Unit of charge

= 9652.19	aC
= 26.812	A·h
= 96.522	kC

fathom (–)
UK nautical unit of length

= 182.88	cm
= 0.090 909	chain (surveyor or Gunter's)
= 0.06	chain (engineer or Ramden's)
= 6	ft
= 1.828	m
= 0.363 636	rod, pole or perch

fermi (–)
Unit of length

= 1 × 10^{-15}	m (= 1 femtometre)

firkin (UK)
Unit of volume or capacity

= 40.914	L
= 9	gal (UK)

firkin (US)
Unit of volume or capacity

= 34.068	L
= 9	gal (US)

foot (ft)
Unit of length

= 30.48	cm
= 0.015 151	chain (surveyor or Gunter's)
= 0.01	chain (engineer or Ramden's)
= 0.166 66	fathom
= 1.515 15	link (surveyor or Gunter's)
= 1	link (engineer or Ramden's)
= 0.3048	m
= 304.8	mm
= 304 800.0	μm
= 12 000	mils
= 0.0606	rod, pole or perch
= 0.333	yd

foot of air (60°F, 1 atm)
Unit of pressure
=	3.608×10^{-5}	atm
=	0.001 08	inHg (32°F)
=	0.014 692	inH_2O (60°F)
=	3.6585	Pa
=	$5.302\ 72 \times 10^{-4}$	lbf / in^2 (psi)

foot of mercury (ftHg, 32°F)
Unit of pressure
=	40.637	kPa
=	5.894	lbf / in^2 (psi)
=	13.609	ftH_2O (60°F)

foot of water (ftH₂0, 39.2°F)
Unit of pressure
=	0.029 88	bar
=	2.242	cmHg (0°C)
=	29 890.0	dyn / cm^2
=	30.749	gf / cm_2
=	2.989	kPa
=	0.453 52	lbf / in^2 (psi)

foot per hour (ft / h)
Unit of velocity
=	0.508	cm / min
=	0.3048	m / h
=	3.048×10^{-4}	km / h
=	1.894	mi / h

foot per minute (ft / min)
Unit of velocity
=	0.508	cm / s
=	0.018 288	km / h
=	0.011 363 63	mi / h
=	0.3048	m / min
=	0.005 08	m / s

foot per second (ft / s)
Unit of velocity
=	30.48	cm / s
=	43 200	in / h
=	1.097 28	km / h
=	0.018 288	km / min
=	0.592 484	knot
=	18.288	m / min
=	0.681 818	mi / h
=	0.011 363 63	mi / min

foot per second squared (ft / s²)
Unit of acceleration
=	1.097 28	km / (h·s)
=	0.681 818	mi / (h·s)
=	0.3048	m / s^2

	Supplementary units		
1 ft / bbl	=	1.9172	m / m^3
1 ft / °F	=	0.548 64	m / K
1 ft / (UK) gal	=	67.049 41	m / m^3
1 ft / (US) gal	=	80.519 64	m / m^3
1 ft / s^2	=	1.0973	km / (h·s)

	foot — examples of foreign units					
1 ft	South Africa	=	1.033 ft (UK)	=	31.48 cm
1 ft^2	" "	=	1.067 ft^2 (UK)	=	9.914 dm^2
1 ft^3	" "	=	1.103 ft^3 (UK)	=	31.23 dm^3
1 ft	Mauritius	=	1.066 ft (UK)	=	32.48 cm
1 ft (fot)	Sweeden	=	11.7 in (UK)	=	29.69 cm
1 ft (fut)	USSR	=	1 ft (UK)	=	30.48 cm

footcandle (fc)
Unit of illuminance or luminous flux density

=	10.763 91	lm / m^2
=	10.763 91	lx (lux)
=	1.076 391	mph (milliphot)
=	0.001 076 391	ph (phot)

foot-lambert (ft·La)
Unit of luminance

=	3.426 259	cd / m^2
=	3.426 259	nits
=	1.076 391	mLa (millilambert)
=	1.076 391 × 10^{-3}	La
=	3.426 259 × 10^{-4}	sb (stilb)
=	1	lm / ft^2

foot pound-force (ft·lbf)
Unit of energy

=	0.001 286	Btu
=	1.355 82 × 10^7	erg
=	1.355 82	J or Nm or W·s

	Supplementary units		
ft·lbf / (UK) gal	=	0.298 474	kJ / m^3
ft·lbf / (US) gal	=	0.358 169	kJ / m^3
ft·lbf / min	=	225 970.0	erg / s
ft·lbf / lb	=	2.9891	J / kg
ft·lbf / (lb·°F)	=	5.3803	J / (kg·K)
ft·lbf / s	=	1.356	W
ft·pdl	=	0.042 133	J or W·s
"	=	421 400.0	erg
ft^2 / h	=	2.581 × 10^{-5}	m^2 / s
ft^4 (fourth power)	=	8.631 × 10^{-3}	m^4
ft·lbf / (ft^2·min)	=	1.569 × 10^{-4}	W / in^2

franklin (Fr)
Unit of electric charge
  = 1   sC   (statcoulomb)

franklin per second (Fr / s)
Unit of electric current
  = 1   sA   (statampere)
  = 333.564   pA   (picoampere)

free fall (−)
Unit of acceleration
  = 32.174   ft / s^2
  = 9.806 65   m / s^2

french foot or pied français (pif)
Unit of length
  = 1.065 75   ft
  = 1.065 75   engineer's link
  = 32.484   cm

furlong (−)
Unit of length
  = 201.168   m

— G —

Gal (galileo)
Unit of acceleration

=	0.01	m / s^2
=	1	cm / s^2

gallon (UK, CAN, or Imp gal)
Unit of volume and capacity

=	4.546 090	L or dm^3
=	4 546.090	mL or cm^3
=	1.200 95	gal (US)
=	160	oz fl
=	153.722	oz (US fl)
=	8	pt
=	4	qt
=	4.8038	qt (US liq.)
=	32	gills
=	0.111	firkin

gallon (UK) per acre (−)
Unit of volume per area

=	1.123 36	cm^3 / m^2
=	11.2336	dm^3 / ha or L / ha

gallon (UK) per cubic foot (gal / ft^3)
Unit of volume per volume

=	160.5437	dm^3 / m^3 or L / m^3

gallon (UK) per day
Flow rate (volume basis)

=	0.052 615	cm^3 / s or mL / s
=	0.004 546 09	m^3 / d or kL / d
=	52.615	mm^3 or μL / s

gallon (UK) per hour
Flow rate (volume basis)

=	4.459 54 × 10^{-5}	ft^3 / s
=	109.099	L / d
=	1.2628	mL / s

gallon (UK) per hour foot [gal / (h·ft)]
Flow rate per length (volume basis)
= 4.143 055 × 10^{-6} m^2 / s or m^3 / (s·m)

gallon (UK) per hour inch [gal / (h·in)]
Flow rate per length (volume basis)
= 4.971 667 × 10^{-5} m^2 / s or m^3 / (s·m)

gallon (UK) per minute foot [gal / (min·ft)]
Flow rate per length (volume basis)
= 2.485 833 × 10^{-4} m^2 / s or m^3 / (s·m)

gallon (UK) per hour square foot [gal / (h·ft^2)]
Flow rate per area (volume basis)
= 1.359 270 × 10^{-5} m / s or m^3 / (s·m^2)

gallon (UK) per mile (gal / mi)
Unit of fuel consumption

=	2.824 821	L / km
=	282.482	L / 100 km

gallon (UK) per minute (gal / min)
Flow rate (volume basis)

=	1.7143	bbl / h
=	0.272 765	m^3 / h
=	75.768 12	mL / s
=	0.001 44	Mgal (UK) / d

gallon (UK) of water per minute (62°F)
Flow rate (mass basis)

=	6531.73	kg / d
=	75.599	g / s
=	14 400	lb / d
=	2.667	oz (avdp) / s

gallon (UK) of water (gal H_2O)
Unit of volume per mass (weight)

=	4.5458	kg (4°C)
=	4.5416	kg (15.5°C)
=	10.0219	lb (39.2°F)
=	10.012	lb (60°F)

gallon (UK) of water per pound (gal H_2O / lb)
Unit of volume per mass (weight)

=	10.022 41	L / kg or mL / g
=	0.160 544	ft^3 / lb

gallon (UK) per second (gal / s)
Flow rate (volume basis)

=	102.85	bbl / h
=	4546.09	cm^3 / s
=	9.6326	ft^3 / min
=	16.3659	m^3 / h
=	0.356 76	yd^3 / min

Supplementary units		
gal (UK) / ton	=	4.474 409 dm^3 / t or L / t
gal (UK) / tn	=	5.012 128 dm^3 / t or L / t
gal (UK) / 1000 bbl	=	28.594 03 cm^3 / m^3
gal (UK) / (avdp) oz	=	2.568 697 ft^3 / lb

gallon (US gal)
Unit of volume and capacity

=	3.785 412	L or dm^3
=	3785.412	mL or cm^3
=	0.832 675	gal (UK)
=	128	oz fl
=	133.23	oz (UK fl)
=	8	pt
=	4	qt
=	3.3307	qt (UK liq.)

gallon (US gal dry)
Unit of volume

=	0.038 095 592	bbl (US dry)
=	0.036 941 181	bbl (US liq.)
=	0.125	bu (US)
=	0.003 472 2	chaldron
=	4404.883	cm^3
=	0.155 57	ft^3
=	268.8025	in^3
=	0.005 761 371	yd^3
=	0.129 294	firkin
=	1.163 647 2	gal (US liq.)
=	4.404 760	L
=	148.947	oz (US fl)
=	0.5	peck
=	8	pt (US dry)
=	4	qt (US dry)
=	4.654 488 7	qt (US liq.)

gallon (US) per acre (–)
Unit of volume per area

=	0.935 394	cm^3 / m^2
=	9.392 54	dm^3 / ha or L / ha

gallon (US) per cubic foot (gal / ft³)
Unit of volume per volume

=	133.681	dm^3 / m^3 or L / m^3

gallon (US) per day (gal / d)
Flow rate (volume basis)

=	$4.381\ 264 \times 10^{-8}$	m^3 / s
=	0.043 812 64	cm^3 / s or mL / s
=	0.003 786	m^3 / d or kL / d
=	43.813	mm^3 / s or $\mu L / s$
=	$4.381\ 264 \times 10^{-5}$	dm^3 / s or L / s

gallon (US) per hour (gal / h)
Flow rate (volume basis)

=	$3.068\ 883 \times 10^{-6}$	acre ft
=	$5.114\ 806 \times 10^{-8}$	acre ft / min
=	$8.524\ 676 \times 10^{-10}$	acre ft / s
=	$3.682\ 659 \times 10^{-5}$	acre in / h
=	0.133 681	ft^3 / h
=	$2.228\ 009 \times 10^{-3}$	ft^3 / min
=	$3.713\ 349 \times 10^{-5}$	ft^3 / s
=	$6.309\ 020 \times 10^{-5}$	m^3 / min
=	$1.051\ 503 \times 10^{-6}$	m^3 / s
=	90.487 34	L / d or dm^3 / d
=	1.051 48	mL / s or cm^3 / s

gallon (US) per hour foot [gal / (h·ft)]
Flow rate per length (volume basis)

=	3.45×10^{-6}	m^2 / s or $m^3 / (s \cdot m)$

gallon (US) per hour square foot [gal / (h·ft²)]
Flow rate per area (volume basis)

=	1.132×10^{-5}	m / s or $m^3 / (s \cdot m^2)$

gallon (US) per mile (gal / mi)
Fuel consumption
=	2.352 146	L / km
=	235.2146	L / 100 km

gallon (US) per minute (gal / min)
Flow rate (volume basis)
=	$4.419\ 190 \times 10^{-3}$	acre ft / d
=	$2.209\ 590 \times 10^{-3}$	acre in / h
=	63.091	cm^3 / s or mL / s
=	8.020 833	ft^3 / h
=	0.133 680 5	ft^3 / min
=	$2.228\ 001 \times 10^{-3}$	ft^3 / s
=	1 440	gal (US) / d
=	60	gal (US) / h
=	0.063 088 43	L / s or dm^3 / s
=	0.001 44	Mgal / d
=	3.785 306	L / min
=	1.2846	bbl (oil) / h
=	0.227 124	m^3 / h

gallon (US) of water (gal $H_2$0)
Unit of mass
=	3.785 31	kg of $H_2$0 (3.98°C)
=	3.781 68	kg of $H_2$0 (15.6°C)
=	8.345 17	lb of $H_2$0 (39.2°F)
=	8.337 17	lb of $H_2$0 (60°F)

gallon (US) of water (60°F) per minute (–)
Flow rate (mass basis)
=	12 005.5	lb of $H_2$0 / d
=	500.230	lb of $H_2$0 / hr
=	8.337 17	lb of $H_2$0 / min
=	0.138 953	lb of $H_2$0 / s
=	6.002 76	tn of $H_2$0 / d

Supplementary Units		
gal (US) / lb	= 8.345 51	L / kg or mL / g
"	= 0.133 681	ft^3 / lb
gal (US) / 1000 bbl	= 23.809 52	cm^3 / m^3
gal (US) / 1000 ft^3	= 3.166 910	dm^3 / kmol
gal (US) / ton (long)	= 3.725 627	dm^3 / t or L / t
gal (US) / tn (short)	= 4.172 702	dm^3 / t or L / t

gallon – examples of foreign units					
1 gal – Barbados	= 0.832 67 gal (UK)	= 3.785 33	L
" Cuba	= 0.832 67 " "	= 3.785 33	"
" El Salvador	= 0.832 67 " "	= 3.785 33	"
" Haiti	= 0.82 " "	= 3.75	"
" Peru	= 1 " "	= 4.546	"
" Honduras	= 0.760 " "	= 3.456	"

1 gal (UK)	= 1.200 95 gal (US)	= 4.546 092 L
1 gal (US)	= 0.832 67 gal (UK)	= 3.785 306 L

gamma (γ)
Unit of magnetic flux

= 1	nT	(nanotesla)
= 1 × 10⁻⁹	T	
= 1	μg (microgram)	
= 1 × 10⁻⁶	kg	

gauss (Gs)
Unit of magnetic flux density

= 1	Mx / cm²	
= 0.1	mT (militesla) = 10⁻⁴ T	

geepound (−)
Unit of mass

= 14.594	kg
= 1	slug

gigajoule (GJ)
Unit of energy

= 277.8	kW·h
= 1000	MJ
= 9.48	therms

gigawatt-hour (GW·h)
Unit of power

= 1 × 10⁶	kW·h	(kilowatt-hour)	= 1 × 10³	W·h
= 1 × 10³	MW·h	(megawatt-hour)	= 1 × 10⁶	W·h
= 1 × 10⁻³	TW·h	(terawatt-hour)	= 1 × 10¹²	W·h

gilbert (Gb)
Unit of magnetomotive force, magnetic potential

= 0.795 78	At
= 1	cgs emu of electric potential
= 3 × 10¹⁰	cgs esu
= 10	pragilberts

Supplementary units		
Gb / cm =	0.079 577 472	aAt / cm
" =	0.795 774	At / cm
" =	1	Oe (oersted)
Gb / Mx =	7.9548 × 10⁷	At / Wb
" =	1	cgs emu of reluctance
" =	8.988 × 10²⁰	cgs esu

gill (gi)
Unit of capacity (UK)

= 142.065	cm³ or mL
= 5	oz (UK fl)

gill (gi)
Unit of capacity (US)

= 118.295	cm³ or mL
= 4	oz (US fl)
= 4.1634	oz (UK fl)

grade (...^{g})
Unit of angular measure

= 100	...^{c}	(centesimal minutes)
= 0.9	...^{o}	(degree)
= 54	...$'$	(minute)
= 0.01	...^{L}	(quadrant)
= 0.015 708	rad	(radian)
= 0.0025	...^{r}	(revolution)
= 3240	...$''$	(second)

Supplementary units		
...^{g} / h	= 2.5000 × 10^{-4}	...^{o} / s
"	= 4.3634 × 10^{-6}	rad / s
"	= 6.9444 × 10^{-7}	...^{r} / s
...^{g} / min	= 0.015	...^{o} / s
"	= 2.6180 × 10^{-4}	rad / s
"	= 4.1666 × 10^{-4}	...^{r} / s
...^{g} / s	= 0.9	...^{o} / s
"	= 0.0157	rad / s
"	= 0.0025	...^{r} / s

grain (gr)
Unit of mass (apoth. or troy)

    = 64.799   mg

Supplementary units		
gr / ft^3	= 2.288 352	g / m^3 or mg / L
"	= 2.282 352 × 10^{-3}	mg / cm^3 or mg / mL
"	= 2.285 714 × 10^{-3}	oz / ft^3
"	= 3.857 143 × 10^{-3}	lb / yd^3
"	= 1.428 571 × 10^{-4}	lb / ft^3
"	= 3.666 667 × 10^{-4}	oz / (UK) gal
"	= 3.055 100 × 10^{-4}	oz / (US) gal
gr / (UK) gal	= 14.2538	g / m^3
"	= 0.832 673	gr / (US) gal
"	= 2.285 710 × 10^{-3}	oz / (UK) gal
"	= 1.903 261 × 10^{-3}	oz / (US) gal
gr / (US) gal	= 17.1181	g / m^3
"	= 1.200 95	gr / (UK) gal
"	= 2.745 030 × 10^{-3}	oz / (UK) gal
"	= 2.285 710 × 10^{-3}	oz / (US) gal

grain – examples of foreign units			
1 gr – India	=	64.798 91	mg
"	Pakistan	=	64.798 91	mg
"	"	=	1	gr (US)
"	Mauritius	=	53.115	mg
"	Seychelles	=	53.1148	mg
"	"	=	0.82	gr (UK)

gram (g)
Unit of energy used in atomic physics

= 8.9875 × 10^{13}	J	(Joule)
= 8.9875 × 10^{20}	erg	(erg)
= 6.0225 × 10^{23}	u	(atomic mass unit)
= 4.1233 × 10^{31}	Ry	(rydberg)
= 5.6099 × 10^{32}	eV	(electronvolt)
= 4.5248 × 10^{36}	cm^{-1}	(reciprocal centimetre)
= 6.5102 × 10^{36}	K	(kelvin)
= 1.3565 × 10^{47}	s^{-1}	(reciprocal second)

gram (g)
Unit of mass

= 15.432	gr
= 0.001	kg
= 1 × 10^{-6}	Mg or t
= 0.032 150 73	oz (apoth.)
= 0.035 273 96	oz (avdp)

gram-calorie (g·cal)
Unit of energy

= 4.184	J or W·s
= 4.184 × 10^7	erg

gram-calorie per second (g·cal / s)
Unit of power

= 14.28	Btu / h
= 4.184	W

gram-centimetre (g·cm)
Unit of energy

= 980.665	erg
= 9.806 65 × 10^{-5}	J

gram centimetre per gram (g·cm / g)
Unit of energy per mass

= 9.806 65 × 10^{-5}	J / g
= 2.724 × 10^{-8}	W·h / g

gram-centimetre per second (g·cm / s)
Unit of energy or power

= 9.301 × 10^{-8}	Btu / s
= 9.806 65 × 10^{-5}	J / s or W

gram-force (gf)
Unit of force

= 980.665	dyn
= 9.806 65 × 10^{-3}	N
= 1 × 10^{-6}	Mgf or tf

gram-force per square centimetre (gf / cm²)
Unit of pressure

= 9.806 65 × 10^{-4}	bar
= 10	kgf / m²
= 98.0665	Pa

gram-mole (g·mol)
Unit of amount of substance

= 22.4	L	(0°C, 1 atm)
= 23.7	L	(15.5°C, 1 atm)
= 24.5	L	(25°C, 1 atm)

gram per centimetre (g / cm)
Unit of mass per length

= 100	kg / km
= 354.8	lb / mi
= 0.1	Mg / km or t / km

gram per centimetre second [g / (cm·s)]
Unit of dynamic viscosity

= 100	cP (centipoise)
= 0.1	Pa·s
= 0.0672	lb / (ft·s)

gram per cubic centimetre (g / cm³)
Unit of density or concentration

= 1	kg / dm^3 or kg / L
= 1	mg / mm^3 or $mg / \mu L$
= 1	Mg / m^3 or t / m^3
= 1000	kg / m^3 or kg / kL
= 1000	mg / cm^3 or mg / mL
= 437 000.0	gr / ft^3
= 1685.5	lb / yd^3
= 998.84	oz / ft^3
= 160.22	oz / (UK) gal
= 133.526	oz / (US) gal
= 62.427	lb / ft^3
= 10.02	lb / (UK) gal
= 8.345	lb / (US) gal
= 0.842 77	tn / yd^3
= 0.752 48	ton / yd^3
= 0.578 04	oz / in^3
= $3.612\ 73 \times 10^{-2}$	lb / in^3

gram per cubic decimetre (g / dm³)
Unit of density or concentration

= 70.161	gr / (UK) gal
= 58.417	gr / (US) gal
= 0.001	g / cm^3 or g / mL
= 0.001	kg / dm^3 or kg / kL
= 0.001	mg / mm^3 or $mg / \mu L$
= 1	kg / m^3 or kg / kL
= 1	mg / cm^3 or mg / mL
= 0.062 43	lb / ft^3
= 10.02	lb / 1000 (UK) gal
= 8.345	lb / 1000 (US) gal
= 0.001	Mg / m^3 or t / m^3

gram per cubic metre (g / m³)
Unit of density or concentration

= 0.437	gr / ft³
= 0.070 136	gr / (UK) gal
= 0.058 418	gr / (US) gal
= 1 × 10⁻⁶	g / cm³ or μg / m³
= 1 × 10⁻³	mg / cm³ or mg / mL
= 1.611 × 10⁻⁴	oz / (UK) gal
= 1.335 × 10⁻⁴	oz / (US) gal

gram per (UK) gallon (g / gal)
Unit of mass per volume

= 0.219 969 2	kg / m³

gram per (US) gallon (g / gal)
Unit of mass per volume

= 0.264 172 8	kg / m³

gram per litre (g / L)
Unit of mass per volume
(See gram per cubic decimetre)

gram per square metre (g / m²)
Unit of mass per area

= 3.227 × 10⁻³	oz / ft²
= 0.0929	g / ft²
= 1000	kg / km²
= 1000	mg / m²
= 2.856	tn / mi²
= 1	Mg / km²
= 1	t / km²

Supplementary units		
1 g / t (metric) =	1	mg / kg
" " =	0.002	lb / tn
" " =	0.002 240	lb / ton
1 g / tn (short) =	1.1023	mg / kg
1 g / ton (long) =	0.984 206	mg / kg

gram-rad (g·rad)
Unit of energy

= 1 × 10⁻⁵	J

gravitational constants
Unit of acceleration

= 980.665	cm / s²
= 32.174	ft / s²
= 35.304	km / (h·s)
= 9.806 65	m / s²

gravity (standard)
Same as gravitational constants

gray (Gy)
Unit of absorbed dose (radiology)

= 1	J / kg
= 100	rads

(1 Gy / s = 1 W / kg)

– H –

hectare (ha)
Unit of area
= 2.471 054		acres
= 0.01		km^2
= 10 000		m^2
= 11 960		yd^2
= 107 639.1		ft^2
= 3.861 022 × 10^{-3}		mi^2

hectolitre (hL)
Unit of capacity
= 10	dal
= 100	L
= 0.1	m^3
= 21.997 55	gal (UK)
= 26.417 94	gal (US)
= 22.703	gal (US dry)

henry (H)
Unit of electric inductance
= 1	V / (A·s)
= 1	Wb / A
= 1 × 10^8	lines / A
= 1 × 10^9	aH (abhenry) or cgs emu
= 1	cgs unit of inductance
= 1.112 65 × 10^{-12}	cgs esu or sH

henry per metre (H / m)
Unit of permeability
= 2.54 × 10^6	lines per ampere inch
= 795 775	Gs / Oe (gauss per oersted)
= 795 775	cgs units of permeability
= 795 775	cgs emu
= 8.854 16 × 10^{-16}	cgs esu

hogshead (UK)
Unit of volume or capacity
= 0.245 489	m^3
= 52.458	gal (UK)

hogshead (US)
Unit of volume or capacity
= 0.238 842	m^3
= 63	gal (US)
= 63	gal (wine)
= 1.5	bbl of oil (US)

horsepower (hp)
Unless otherwise designated, the term horsepower refers to
mechanical horsepower, which is equal to 550 ft·lbf / s

=	2546.14	Btu / h
=	42.436	Btu / min
=	0.707 260	Btu / s
=	640 693.0	cal / h
=	1 980 000.0	ft·lbf / h
=	745.577	J / s
=	0.745 577	kW

horsepower (boiler)
Unit of power

=	33 493.8	Btu / h
=	13.1548	hp
=	9809.5	J / s
=	9.8095	kW
=	34.5	lb of H_2O evaporated / h (from and at 212°F)

horsepower (electric)
Unit of power

=	2547.16	Btu / h
=	640 951.0	cal / h
=	0.076 648	hp (boiler)
=	1.014 277	hp (metric)
=	746	J / s or W

horsepower (metric)
Also designated as cheval-vapeur (CV) or pferdestaerke (PS)

=	2511.3	Btu / h
=	735.5	W

horsepower (water)

=	33 015.2	ft·lbf / min
=	3960	gal (US)·ft / min
=	1	hp (electric)
=	746.92	W

horsepower per ton of refrigeration
US commercial

=	0.212 039	(coefficient of performance)$^{-1}$
=	24	hp·h / ton·d of refrigeration

horsepower-hour per ton-day of refrigeration

=	$8.834\ 97 \times 10^{-3}$	(coefficient of performance)$^{-1}$
=	$4.166\ 66 \times 10^{-2}$	hp / ton of refrigeration
=	273 745.0	kg·m / (ton·d) of refrig.
=	0.745 700	kW·h / (ton·d) of refrig.

hour, mean solar (h)
Unit of time

= 0.041 666	d	(mean solar)	
= 60	min	"	"
= 0.001 369 863	mo (mean)	"	"
= 0.001 388 889	mo (30 d)	"	"
= 0.001 344 086	mo (31 d)	"	"
= 0.005 952 381	week	(mean calendar)	
= 0.000 114 115 25	yr	(calendar)	
= 0.000 114 079 55	yr	(sideral)	
= 0.000 114 079 55	yr	(tropical)	

hundredweight (UK cwt)
Unit of mass

= 50.802 35	kg
= 0.05	ton
= 0.056	tn (short ton)
= 0.508 023 50	t (tonne)

hundredweight (US cwt)
Unit of mass

= 45.359 24	kg
= 0.044 642 86	ton
= 0.05	tn
= 0.045 359 24	t

– I –

inch (in)
Unit of length

=	2.54	cm
=	0.083 333	ft
=	25.4	mm
=	1000	mils
=	25 400.0	μm
=	0.027 777	yd
=	0.0254	m
=	2.54×10^{-7}	nm

inch of air (60°F, 1 atm)
Unit of pressure

=	0.304 654	N / m^2 or Pa
=	0.083 333	ft of air (60°F, 1 atm)
=	1.0203×10^{-4}	ft of H$_2$0 (60°F)
=	8.9970×10^{-5}	in of Hg (32°F)
=	1.2244×10^{-3}	in of H$_2$0 (60°F)
=	6.3632×10^{-3}	lbf / ft^2 (psf)
=	4.4189×10^{-5}	lbf / in^2 (psi)

inch of mercury (inHg, 32°F)
Unit of pressure

=	0.033 421 1	atm
=	0.033 864	bar
=	33 863.9	dyn / cm^2
=	3386.38	N / m^2 or Pa
=	926.24	ft of air (60°F, 1 atm)
=	1.132 957	ft of H$_2$0 (39.2°F)
=	34.5316	gf / cm^2
=	0.034 531 6	kgf / cm^2
=	345.316	kgf / m^2
=	1131.62	oz / ft^2
=	7.858 47	oz / in^2
=	70.7262	lbf / ft^2 (psf)
=	0.491 154	lbf / in^2 (psi)

inch of water (inH$_2$0, 39.2°F)
Unit of pressure

=	2.4582×10^{-3}	atm
=	2490.82	dyn / cm^2
=	2.54	gf / cm^2
=	2.491	mbar (millibar)
=	1.87	mmHg (0°C)
=	0.024 91	N / cm^2
=	249.082	Pa
=	0.0254	tf / m^2

Supplementary units

in / °F	=	4.572	cm / °C
in / h	=	0.042 333	cm / min
"	=	$7.055\ 555 \times 10^{-4}$	cm / s
"	=	$1.388\ 889 \times 10^{-3}$	ft / min
"	=	$2.314\ 482 \times 10^{-5}$	ft / s
"	=	$2.777\ 778 \times 10^{-4}$	in / s
"	=	$1.578\ 282 \times 10^{-5}$	mi / h
"	=	$2.630\ 471 \times 10^{-7}$	mi / min
"	=	$4.384\ 119 \times 10^{-9}$	mi / s
in / min	=	152.4	cm / h
"	=	0.042 333	cm / s
"	=	5	ft / h
"	=	0.083 333	ft / min
"	=	0.001 388	ft / s
"	=	$9.469\ 690 \times 10^{-4}$	mi / h
"	=	$1.578\ 282 \times 10^{-5}$	mi / min
"	=	$2.630\ 471 \times 10^{-7}$	mi / s
in / s	=	9144	cm / h
"	=	152.4	cm / min
"	=	2.54	cm / s
"	=	300	ft / h
"	=	5	ft / min
"	=	0.083 333	ft / s
"	=	3600	in / h
"	=	0.056 818	mi / h
"	=	$9.469\ 690 \times 10^{-4}$	mi / min
"	=	$1.578\ 282 \times 10^{-5}$	mi / s
in / s^2	=	0.0254	m / s^2
in^4 (4th power)	=	41.623 143	cm^4
"	=	$4.162\ 31 \times 10^{-7}$	m^4

inch – examples of foreign units

1 in – Turkey	=	1.240	in (UK)	=	3.138 cm
"	Swaziland	=	1.033	in (UK)	=	2.624 cm
"	El Salvador	=	0.913	in (UK)	=	2.320 cm

– J –

joule (J)
Unit of energy including work and quantity of heat

= 1	N·m	(newton metre)
= 1	V·C	(volt coulomb)
= 1	W·s	(watt-second)
= $9.470\ 88 \times 10^{-4}$	Btu	
= 0.238 662	cal	
= 1×10^7	dyn·cm or erg	
= 10 197.16	g·cm	
= 0.737 562	ft·lbf	
= 23.731	ft·pdl	

		Supplementary units	
J / Å	=	1×10^{10}	J / m
J / cm³	=	26.84	Btu / ft³
"	=	238.846	kcal / m³
J / (cm³·K)	=	14.9107	Btu / (ft³·°F)
"	=	238.846	kcal / (m³·°C)
J / C	=	1	V
J / °C	=	5.2692×10^{-4}	Btu / °F
J / g	=	0.429 923	Btu / lb
"	=	0.238 846	kcal / kg
J / (g·°C)	=	0.239	Btu / (lb·°F)
"	=	0.239	cal / (g·°C)
J / kg	=	0.1084	cal / lb
J / L	=	0.0269	Btu / ft³
"	=	1	kJ / m³
J / mol	=	0.43	Btu / (lb·mol)
"	=	0.101 97	kg·m / cm³
J / s	=	0.056 907	Btu / min
"	=	14.241	cal / min
"	=	1	W
J / T	=	1	A / m²

joule (J)
Unit of energy used in atomic physics

= 1.1126×10^{-14}	g	(gram)
= 1×10^7	erg	(erg)
= 6.7011×10^9	u	(atomic mass unit)
= 4.5878×10^{17}	Ry	(rydberg)
= 6.2418×10^{18}	eV	(electronvolt)
= 5.0345×10^{22}	cm⁻¹	(reciprocal centimetre)
= 7.2435	K	(kelvin)
= 1.5093	s⁻¹	(reciprocal second)

– K –

katal (kat)
Unit for the measurement of enzymic activity
= 1   mol / s

kayser (–)
Unit of wave number
= 100 m^{-1} (reciprocal metre)

kelvin (K)
Base unit of thermodynamic temperature. (See temperature)

kelvin per metre (K / m)
Unit of temperature per length
= 54.864   °F / 100 ft

kelvin (K)
Unit of energy used in atomic physics

= 1.5361×10^{-37}	g	(gram)
= 1.3806×10^{-23}	J	(joule)
= 1.3806×10^{-16}	erg	(erg)
= 9.2509×10^{-14}	u	(atomic mass unit)
= 6.3336×10^{-6}	Ry	(rydberg)
= 8.6171×10^{-5}	eV	(electronvolt)
= 6.9513×10^{-1}	cm^{-1}	(reciprocal centimetre)
= 2.0836×10^{10}	s^{-1}	(reciprocal second)

kilderkin (UK)
Unit of volume or capacity

= 0.5	barrel	(UK)
= 2	firkins	(UK)
= 18	gal	(UK)
= 81.828	L	

kilocalorie (kcal or Cal)
Unit of energy

= 3.968	Btu
= 4.186	kJ
= 1.163	W·h

Supplementary units		
$kcal_{(IT)}$ / m^3	= 4.184	kJ / m^3 or mJ / cm^3
$kcal_{(tc)}$ / (m^3·°C)	= 0.062 428	Btu / (ft^3·°F)
"	= 4.1868	mJ / (cm^3·K)
$kcal_{(tc)}$ / (g·mol)	= 4.184	kJ / mol
$kcal_{(tc)}$ / h	= 1.163	W
$kcal_{(tc)}$ / (h·m^2·°C)	= 1.163	W / (m^2·K)
$kcal_{(tc)}$ / (h·m^2·°C) / m	= 1.163	W / (m·K)
$kcal_{(tc)}$ / kg	= 1.8	Btu / (lb)
"	= 4.1868	J / g
"	= 426.935	kgf·m / kg
$kcal_{(tc)}$ / (kg·°C)	= 1	Btu / (lb·°F)
"	= 4.1868	J / g
$kcal_{(tc)}$ / (m·h·°C)	= 0.671 97	Btu / (ft·h·°F)
"	= 0.011 63	W / (cm·K)

kilogram (kg)
Base unit of mass

= 10 000	dg	(decigram)
= 100	dag	(decagram)
= 1000	g	
= 1 000 000	mg	
= 32.150 74	oz	(apoth.)
= 35.273 96	oz	(avdp)
= 2.679 229	lb	(apoth.)
= 2.204 623	lb	(avdp)
= $9.842\ 065 \times 10^{-4}$	ton	
= $1.102\ 311 \times 10^{-3}$	tn	
= 0.001	t	

kilogram per cubic decimetre (kg / dm³)
Unit of mass per volume or density

= 10.022 42	lb / gal	(UK)
= 8.345 406	lb / gal	(US)
= 62.427 97	lb / ft³	

kilogram per cubic metre (kg / m³)
Unit of mass per volume or density

= 0.001	g / cm³
= 0.062 428	lb / ft³
= 1.685 555	lb / yd³
= $7.524\ 499 \times 10^{-4}$	ton / yd³
= $8.427\ 775 \times 10^{-4}$	tn / yd³
= 0.001	t / m³

kilogram per hectare (kg / ha)
Unit of mass per area

= 1×10^{-5}	g / cm²
= 0.1	g / m²

kilogram per hour (kg / h)
Unit of mass flow rate

= 2.204 62	lb / h
= 0.036 743 710	lb / min
= $6.123\ 952 \times 10^{-4}$	lb / s

kilogram per kilometre (kg / km)
Unit of mass per length

= 0.391 982	gr / in
= 0.01	g / cm
= 0.0254	g / in
= 0.001	kg / m
= $6.719\ 689 \times 10^{-4}$	lb / ft
= 5.6	lb / in
= 3.547 996	lb / mi
= $2.015\ 907 \times 10^{-3}$	lb / yd
= $1.773\ 998 \times 10^{-3}$	tn / mi

kilogram per metre (kg / m)
Unit of mass per length

=	391.982	gr / in
=	25.4	g / in
=	0.671 969	lb / ft
=	0.055 997	lb / in
=	3547.996	lb / mi
=	2.015 901	lb / yd
=	1.773 998	tn / mi
=	1	t / km

kilogram per second (kg / s)
Unit of mass flow rate

=	0.059 052	ton / min
=	0.066 139	tn / min
=	3.543 143	ton / h
=	3.968 320	tn / h
=	85.035 46	ton / d
=	95.239 73	tn / d
=	69.524 98	Mlb / yr
=	3103.793	ton / yr
=	3476.249	tn / yr
=	0.671 969	lb / ft
=	2.204 623	lb / s
=	132.277	lb / min

kilogram per second metre [kg / (s·m)]
Unit of mass flow rate per length

=	0.671 969	lb / (s·ft)
=	2419.088	lb / (h·ft)

kilogram per second square metre [kg / (s·m^2)]
Unit of mass flow rate per area

=	0.204 816	lb / (s·ft^2)
=	737.338	lb / (h·ft^2)

kilogram per square kilometre (kg / km^2)
Unit of mass per area

=	0.001	g / m^2 or Mg / km^2
=	0.0001	mg / cm^2
=	0.008 923	lb / acre
=	0.002 549	ton / mi^2
=	0.022 856	tn / mi^2
=	0.001	t / km^2

kilogram metre per second (kg·m / s)
Unit of momentum

=	7.233	lb·ft / s

kilogram metre per second squared (kg·m / s²)
Unit of force
- = 1   N   (newton)
- = 9.806 65   J / cm²

Supplementary units		
$kg·m^2 / (A·s^3)$	= 1	V
$kg·m^2 / (A·s^2)$	= 1	Wb
$kg·m^2 / (A^2·s^2)$	= 1	H
$kg·m^2 / (A^2·s^3)$	= 1	Ω
$kg·m^2 / s^3$	= 1	W
$kg·m^2 / s^2$	= 1	J

kilogram-force (kg·f)
Unit of force
- = 9.806 65   N

Supplementary units		
kgf / cm	= 980.665	N·m
kgf / m^3	= 9.806 65	N / m^3 or Pa / m
kgf / (kg·°C)	= 9.806 65	N / (kg·K)
kgf / m	= 9.806 65	N / m
kgf / (m·s·°C)	= 9.806 65	$W / (m^2·K)$
kgf / (s·°C)	= 9.806 65	W / (m·K)
kgf / cm^2	= 98.066 5	kPa
kgf / m^2	= 9.806 65	Pa
kgf·m	= 9.806 65	J
kgf·m / kg	= 9.806 65	J / kg
kgf·m / s	= 9.806 65	W
kgf·m·s	= 9.806 65	J·s
kgf·m·s²	= 9.806 65	kg·m²
kgf·s	= 9.806 65	N·s
$kgf·s / m^2$	= 9.806 65	$N·s / m^2$
$kgf·s / m^2$	= 9.806 65	Pa·s
$kgf·s / m^4$	= 9.806 65	kg / m^3

kilojoule (kJ)
Unit of energy
- = 0.947 817   Btu
- = 0.277 778   W·h

kilojoule per cubic metre (kJ / m³)
Unit of energy per volume
- = 0.026 839 $Btu_{(IT)} / ft^3$
- = 0.239 $kcal_{(tc)} / m^3$
- = 0.004 309   Btu / gal   (UK)
- = 0.003 588   Btu / gal   (US)
- = 1 J / dm^3 or J / L

kilojoule per kilogram (kJ / kg)
Unit of energy per mass
- = 0.429 93   Btu / lb
- = 0.239 $cal_{(tc)} / g$

kilojoule per kilogram kelvin [kJ / (kg·K)]
Unit of specific energy capacity (mass basis)
- = 0.2388   Btu / (lb·°F)
- = 0.239   cal / (g·K)
- = 277.778   mW·h / (kg·°C)

kilojoule per kilomole kelvin [kJ / (kmol·K)]
Unit of specific energy
- = 0.238 846 $Btu_{(IT)}$ / (lb·mol·°F)
- = 0.239 $kcal_{(tc)}$ / g·mol)

kilolitre (kL)
Unit of capacity
- = 1000   L or dm^3
- = 219.969   gal (UK)
- = 264.172   gal (US)
- = 1000   kg of H_2O (4°C)
- = 1   Mg of H_2O (4°C) = t of H_2O

kilometre (km)
Unit of length or distance
- = 100 000   cm   (centimetre)
- = 10 000   dm   (decimetre)
- = 100   dam   (decametre)
- = 3280.84   ft
- = 10   hm   (hectometre)
- = 0.001   Mm   (megametre)
- = 1000   m
- = 0.539 957   mi   (nautical)
- = 0.621 371   mi   (statute)

kilometre per hour (km / h)
Unit of velocity or speed
- = 27.777 78   cm / s
- = 3280.839   ft / h
- = 54.6801   ft / min
- = 0.911 344   ft / s
- = 0.539 957   knot
- = 0.621 371   mi / h

kilometre per hour second [km / (h·s)]
Unit of acceleration
- = 27.777 78   cm / s^2 or Gal
- = 0.911 345   ft / s^2

kilomole (kmol)
Unit of amount of substance
- = 836.01 ft^3 (60°F, 1 atm)
- = 22.413 58 m^3 (0°C, 1 atm)
- = 1000   g·mol
- = 2.204 62   lb·mol

kilomole per cubic metre (kmol / m^3)
Unit of amount of substance per volume
- = 133.01 ft^3 / bbl (60°F)
- = 0.062 427   lb·mol / ft^3
- = 0.010 02   lb·mol / (UK) gal
- = 0.008 345 5   lb·mol / (US) gal

kilonewton (kN)

Unit of force

=	0.224 809	kip (1000 lbf)
=	0.100 361	tonf
=	0.112 405	tnf

kilonewton per square metre (kN / m^2)

Unit of force per area

=	20.8834	lbf / ft^2
=	0.145 04	lbf / in^2

kilonewton metre (kN·m)

Unit of bending moment (torque)

=	0.329 369	tonf·ft
=	0.368 781	tnf·ft

kilopascal (kPa)

Unit of pressure or stress

=	0.010 197	at (kgf / cm^2)
=	0.009 869 24	atm (760 torr)
=	10.197 44	cm of H$_2$0 (4°C)
=	0.2953	inHg (32°F)
=	7.500 62	mmHg (0°C)
=	1000	N / m^2
=	20.8834	lbf / ft^2
=	0.145 04	lbf / in^2 (psi)
=	0.010 443	tnf / ft^2

Miscellaneous units			
kPa / m	=	0.044 208	(lbf / in^2) / ft
"	=	4.4208	(lbf / in^2) / 100 ft
kPa·s	=	0.145 038	lbf·s / in^2
kp (kilopond)	=	1	kgf
"	=	9.806 65	N
"	=	70.931	pdl
krad / s	=	1 × 10^6	mrad / s
"	=	159.2	...^{r} / s
ktn (kiloton)	=	1.167	GW·h
kV	=	3.335	sV (statvolt)
kV / cm	=	1 × 10^{11}	μV / m

kilowatt (kW)

Unit of power

=	3414.4	Btu / h	
=	1.3415	hp	(electric)
=	1.342	hp	(mechanical)
=	1.3405	hp	(water)
=	1000	J / s	
=	3.6	MJ / h	

kilowatt-hour (kW·h)

Unit of energy, work

=	3414.4	Btu
=	3.6	MJ
=	3.517	lb of H$_2$0 evaporated from and at 212°F

kilowatt per cubic metre (kW / m³)
Unit of power per volume

=	96.622	$Btu_{(IT)} / (h \cdot ft^3)$
=	0.8604	$cal_{(tc)} / (h \cdot cm^3)$
=	0.037 974	hp / ft^3

kilowatt per cubic metre kelvin [kW / (m³·K)]
Unit of volumetric power transfer coefficient

=	53.679	$Btu_{(IT)} / (h \cdot ft^{3} \cdot °F)$
=	0.014 912	$Btu_{(IT)} / (s \cdot ft^{3} \cdot °F)$

Supplementary units		
$kW / (m \cdot K)$ =	2.39	$cal / (s \cdot cm \cdot °C)$
" =	10	$W / (cm \cdot °C)$
" =	1000	$W / (m \cdot K)$
kW / m^2 =	0.088 05	$Btu_{(IT)} / (s \cdot ft^2)$
" =	86.042	$cal_{(tc)} / (h \cdot cm^2)$
$kW / (m^2 \cdot K)$ =	0.049	$Btu_{(IT)} / (s \cdot ft^{2} \cdot °F)$
" =	86.042	$cal_{(tc)} / (h \cdot cm^{2} \cdot °C)$

Miscellaneous units		
kip (1000 lbf) =	4.448	kN
kip / in^2 =	6.894 757	MPa
kn (knot) =	51.444	cm / s
" =	1.852	km / h
" =	1.150 78	mi / h
" =	0.514 44	m / s
" =	0.030 866	km / min
" =	0.019 179	mi / min

– L –

labor (in California)
Spanish unit of measure

=	173.61	acres
=	7 562 500	ft^2
=	1 000 000	square varas

labor (in Texas)
Spanish unit of measure

=	177.136	acres
=	7 716 049.4	ft^2
=	1 000 000	square varas

lambert (La)
Unit of luminance

=	3183.1	cd / m^2
=	1	lm / cm^2
=	0.318 31	lm / (cm^2·sr)

langley (–)
Unit of power density

=	41 840	J / m^2

last (UK)
Unit of volume

=	26.666	bags
=	80	bushels (UK)
=	2.222 22	chaldrons (UK)
=	20	coombs (UK)
=	102.748	ft^3
=	2.909 496	m^3
=	640	gal (UK)
=	2909.414	L
=	2	loads (UK)
=	10	quarters (UK dry)
=	26.666	sacks or bags
=	10	seams (UK)
=	40	strikes (UK)
=	2	weys (UK, capacity)

last – examples of foreign units			
1 last – Netherlands (volume)	=	660	gal (UK)
" Netherlands (capacity)	=	3000	L
" Netherlands (mass)	=	1.9684	ton (UK)
" Netherlands (mass)	=	2	t (tonne)

league, nautical (UK)
Unit of length

=	18 240	ft
=	5.559 552	km
=	1.000 639	league (naut. Int)
=	1.151 515	league (statute)
=	3	mi (naut. UK)
=	3.454 545	mi (statute)

league, nautical (Int)
Unit of length

=	3038.058	fathoms
=	18 228.346	ft
=	5.556	km
=	0.999 361	league (naut. UK)
=	1.150 779	league (statute)
=	3	mi (naut. Int)
=	3.452 338	mi (statute)

league, statute (–)
Unit of length

=	2640	fathoms
=	15 840	ft
=	4.828 032	km
=	0.868 421 05	league (naut. UK)
=	0.868 976 25	league (naut. Int)
=	2.605 263 2	mi (adm. UK)
=	2.605 263	mi (naut. UK)
=	2.606 928 7	mi (naut. Int)
=	3	mi (statute)

Supplementary units			
1 league	(naut. Int)	= 5.556	km
"	(naut. UK)	= 5.559 552	km
"	(naut. US)	= 5.556	km
"	(stat. US)	= 4.828 032	km
"	(stat. US)	= 3	mi
1 lieue	(Québec)	= 3	mi
"	"	= 4.828 032	km
"	(Mauritius)	= 2.485 42	mi
"	"	= 4	km
"	(Paraguay)	= 2.691	mi
"	"	= 4.33	km
1 legua	(Columbia)	= 5	km
"	(Argentina)	= 5.2	km
"	(Chile)	= 4.514	km
"	(Ecuador)	= 5	km
"	(Guatemala)	= 5.572	km
"	(Honduras)	= 4.174	km
"	(Mexico)	= 4.19	km
"	(Spain)	= 5.572	km
"	(Paraguay)	= 4.33	km
"	(Peru)	= 5.556	km
"	(Brazil)	= 6.6	km
"	(Cuba)	= 4.24	km
1 legua	cuadrada – unit of area		
"	Ecuador	= 31.05	km^2
"	Uruguay	= 26.57	km^2
"	Brazil	= 43.56	km^2
"	Paraguay	= 18.77	km^2

legal subdivision (–)
Unit of area
    = 40   acres
    = 0.161 874   km^2

light year (l·y·)
Unit of length in astronomy
    = 63 239   AU (astronomical unit)
    = 0.3066   pc (parsec)
    = 9.549 94   Pm (petametre)

line (–)
Unit of magnetic flux
    = 1   Mx   (maxwell)
    = 1 × 10^{-8} Wb   (weber)

Supplementary units		
1 line / cm^2 =	1	Gs (gauss)
1 line / in^2 =	0.155	Gs
" =	1.55 × 10^{-5}	T
" =	1.55 × 10^{-9}	Wb / cm^2
" =	1 × 10^{-8}	Wb / in^2

link, surveyor or Gunter's (li)
Unit of length
    = 20.116 84   cm
    = 7.92   in
    = 0.66   ft
    = 0.201 168   m

link, engineer or Ramden's (li)
Unit of length
    = 30.48   cm
    = 12   in
    = 1   ft
    = 0.3048   m

litre (L)
Unit of volume and capacity
    = 1000   cm^3 or mL
    = 1   dm^3
    = 0.001   m^3
    = 61.023 75   in^3
    = 0.219 969   gal   (UK)
    = 0.264 172   gal   (US)
    = 35.196 09   oz   (UK fl)
    = 33.814 97   oz   (US fl)
    = 0.879 902   qt   (UK)
    = 1.056 718   qt   (US)
    = 0.908 11   qt   (US dry)

litre per day (L / d)
Unit of volume (flow rate)
    = 9.166 03 × 10^{-3} gal (UK) / h
    = 1.100 75 × 10^{-2} gal (US) / h

litre per hour (L / h)
Unit of volume (flow rate)
= $3.531\ 566 \times 10^{-2}$ ft^3 / h
= $1.666\ 713 \times 10^{-5}$ m^3 / min

litre per minute (L / min)
Unit of volume (flow rate)
= 0.377 40   bbl / h
= 16.666 cm^3 / s
= 2.118 939 ft^3 / h
= 13.198 14   gal (UK) / h
= 15.849 70   gal (US) / h
= 2.204 62   lb of H_2O / min (4°C)

litre per second (L / s)
Unit of volume (flow rate)
= 22.642   bbl / h
= 0.035 515 ft^3 / s
= 0.078 479 yd^3 / min
= 791.88   gal (UK) / h
= 951.046   gal (US) / h

lumen (lm)
Unit of luminous flux
= 1   cd / sr
= 0.079 58   spherical candle power

Supplementary units		
1 lm / cm^2	= 1	La (lambert)
"	= 1	ph (phot)
"	= 10 000	lx (lux)
1 lm / (cm^2·sr)	= 3.1416	La
1 lm / ft^2	= 1	fc (footcandle)
"	= 1	ft·La
"	= 10.764	lm / m^2 or lx
1 lm / m^2	= 0.093	fc or lm / ft^2
"	= 1	lx
"	= 0.0001	ph
1 lm / sr	= 1	cd

lux (lx)
Unit of illuminance
= 0.092 903 04   fc (footcandle)
= 1   lm / m^2
= 1   cd·sr / m^2
= 0.1   mph (milliphot)
= 1   metre-candle
= 0.0001   ph

– M –

maxwell (Mx)
Unit of magnetic flux

= 1		Gs / cm^2
= 1		line
= 1 × 10^{-8}		Wb or V·s
= 1		cgs emu of induction
= 3.335 64 × 10^{-11}		cgs esu

Supplementary units			
Mx / Gb	=	1.256 64 × 10^{-8}	H or Wb / At
"	=	1	cgs emu of permeance
"	=	1.112 64 × 10^{-21}	cgs esu
Mx / cm^2	=	1	Gs
"	=	6.4516	Mx / in^2

megaelectronvolt sq. centimetre per gram (MeV·cm^2 / g)
Unit of energy

= 1.602 19 × 10^{-14} J·m^2 / kg

megagram (Mg)
Unit of mass

= 1		t (tonne)
= 0.984 206 4		ton
= 1.102 311		tn

megagram per square metre (Mg / m^2)
Unit of mass per area

= 0.091 443 4	ton / ft^2
= 0.102 408 1	tn / ft^2

megajoule (MJ)
Unit of energy

= 0.372 506	hp·h
= 0.277 78	kW·h
= 9.478 17 × 10^{-3}	therm
= 6.984 48 × 10^{-2}	tnf / mi

Supplementary units			
MJ / kg	=	429.92	Btu / lb
MJ / m	=	0.021 289	tnf·mi / ft
MJ / m^3	=	26.839	Btu$_{(IT)}$ / ft^3
"	=	4.308 863	Btu$_{(IT)}$ / (UK) gal
"	=	3.587 878	Btu$_{(IT)}$ / (US) gal
"	=	0.239	cal$_{(tc)}$ / mL

megapascal (MPa)
Unit of pressure

= 9.869 23	atm
= 10	bar
= 1000	kPa
= 0.145 038	kip / in^2
= 9.325	tonf / ft^2
= 10.4427	tnf / ft^2

megawatt (MW)
Unit of power
=	3 412 000	Btu / h
=	102	hp (boiler)

megawatt-hour (MW·h)
Unit of energy and work
=	3.6	GJ (gigajoule)
=	3600	MJ (megajoule)
=	3 600 000	kJ (kilojoule)

mega – Supplementary units			
megerg	=	1×10^6	erg
megaline	=	1×10^6	Mx
megametre	=	1×10^7	dm
"	=	1×10^5	dam
"	=	1×10^6	m
megaparsec	=	1×10^6	pc
megaton	=	1×10^6	tn
megmho	=	1×10^{-3}	abmho
"	=	1×10^6	mhos
"	=	1	microhm^{-1}
megmho / cm	=	1×10^{-3}	abmho / cm
"	=	2.54	megmhos / in^3
"	=	0.166 242	mho·ft / circ. mil
"	=	1	microhm – cm^{-1}
megohm	=	1×10^{15}	abohms
"	=	1×10^{12}	microhms
"	=	1×10^6	ohms
"	=	1.113×10^{-6}	statohm

metre (m)
Base unit of length
=	1×10^{10}	$\overset{\circ}{A}$ (angstrom)
=	0.546 81	fathom
=	3.280 84	ft
=	39.37	in
=	1×10^6	μm (micrometre)
=	1×10^9	nm (nanometre)

metre per cubic metre (m / m³)
Unit of length per volume
=	0.521 612	ft / bbl
=	0.092 903	ft / ft^3
=	0.014 909	ft / (UK) gal
=	0.012 419	ft / (US) gal

metre per hour (m / h)
Unit of velocity or speed
=	1.666 67	cm / min
=	5.4×10^{-4}	kn (knot)
=	6.214×10^{-4}	mi / h

metre per minute (m / min)
Unit of velocity or speed
=	0.054 68	ft / s
=	0.06	km / h

metre per second (m / s)
Unit of velocity or speed
  = 3.6   km / h
  = 2.236 94   mi / h

metre per second squared (m / s^2)
Unit of acceleration
  = 100   cm / s^2 or Gal (galileo)

metre kilogram-force per second (m·kgf / s)
Unit of energy
  = 2.344   cal / s
  = 9.81   W

metre of mercury (mHg, 0°C)
Unit of pressure
  = 1.315 789   atm
  = 1.333 22   bar
  = 44.647   ft of H_2O (60°F)
  = 133.322   kPa
  = 1.359 51   kgf / cm^2
  = 19.336   lbf / in^2

metre of water (mH$_2$0, 4°C)
Unit of pressure
  = 9.806 38   kPa
  = 1.422 29   lbf / in^2

micro – miscellaneous units		
μbar (microbar)	= 0.1	Pa
μcal / (s·cm^2)	= 41.84	mW / m^2
μF (microfarad)	= 1×10^{-15}	aF
μg (microgram)	= 1×10^{-6}	g
"	= 1×10^3	ng
μg / cm^3	= 1×10^{-6}	g / cm^3
"	= 1×10^{-6}	kg / dm^3
"	= 1×10^{-6}	mg / mm^3
μg / m^3	= 1×10^{-6}	g / m^3
"	= 1×10^{-6}	mg / dm^3
μg / mL	= 1×10^{-6}	g / mL
"	= 1×10^{-6}	kg / L
"	= 1×10^{-6}	mg / μL
μJ (microjoule)	= 10	erg
μL (microlitre)	= 1×10^{-9}	m^3
"	= 1	mm^3
μm (micrometre)	= 1×10^{-6}	m
"	= 39.37	μin
"	= 0.039 37	mil
"	= 1	μ (micron)
$\mu\mu$ (micromicron)	= 0.01	Å
"	= 1×10^{-12}	m
"	= 1×10^{-6}	μm
μ (micron)	= 10 000	Å
μV (microvolt)	= 100	aV
"	= 1000	mV
"	= 3.333×10^{-9}	sV
μV / °F	= 1.8	μV / °C
"	= 1	V / °C
μN·m	= 10	dyn·cm
μWb	= 100	Mx
"	= 7.96	unit pole (emu)

mil (–)
Unit of length

= 0.001	in
= 25.4	μm

mile, nautical (Int)
Unit of distance

= 6076.115	ft
= 1.852	km
= 1.150 779	mi (statute)

mile, nautical (UK)
Unit of distance

= 1.853 184	km

mile, statute (mi)
Unit of distance

= 80	chains (surveyor Gunter's)
= 52.8	chains (engineer or Ramden's)
= 5280	ft
= 8	furlongs
= 63 360	in
= 1.609 344	km
= 0.868 976	nautical mile
= 320	rods, poles or perches
= 1760	yd

mile per gallon (UK) *
Fuel consumption

= 0.354 005	km / L or dm^3
= 354 005	m / m^3

mile per gallon (US) *
Fuel consumption

= 0.425 143	km / L or dm^3
= 425 143	m / m^3

* See also gallon per mile

mile per hour (mi / h)
Unit of speed or velocity

= 88	ft / min
= 1.466 67	ft / s
= 17.6	in / s
= 1.609 344	km / h
= 0.868 976	knot (Int)
= 26.822 4	m / min
= 0.447 04	m / s

mile per hour second [mi / (h·s)]
Unit of acceleration

= 44.704	cm / s^2
= 1.466 67	ft / s^2
= 1.609 344	km / (h·s)

mile per minute (mi / min)
Unit of speed or velocity

2682.24	cm / s
= 316 800	ft / h
= 88	ft / s
= 96.560 64	km / h
= 52.138 574	knot (Int)
= 26.822	m / s

mile per second (mi / s)
Unit of speed or velocity

= 5793.63	km / h
= 3128.3	knot (Int)

mile – examples of foreign units

1 mi –	Denmark	= 7.532	km	= 4.681 mi (UK, US)
"	Sweeden	= 10.689	km	= 6.214 mi (UK, US)
"	naut. Int	= 1.852	km	
"	Bohemis Czech.	= 7.003	km	= 4.351 mi (UK, US)
"	Silesia Czech.	= 6.483	km	= 4.028 mi (UK, US)
"	USSR	= 7.47	km	= 4.640 mi (UK, US)

millibar (mbar)
Unit of pressure

= 0.001	bar
= 1000	baryes
= 1000	dyn / cm^2
= 0.750 062	mmHg (0°C)
= 0.01	N / cm^2
= 100	Pa

milligram (mg)
Unit of mass

= 0.015 432	gr
= 0.001	g
= 1 × 10^{-9}	Mg or t (tonne)

milligram per centimetre (mg / cm)
Unit of mass per length

= 0.980 665	dyn / cm
= 0.039 198	gr / in
= 0.002 54	g / in
= 0.1	kg / km

milligram per cubic centimetre (mg / cm^3)
Unit of mass per volume

= 437	gr / ft^3
= 1	oz / ft^3
= 0.160 232	oz / (UK) gal
= 0.133 526	oz / (US) gal
= 0.010 02	lb / (UK) gal
= 0.008 345	lb / (US) gal
= 1	g / dm^3 or kg / m^3 or mg / mL
= 1000	g / m^3 or mg / dm^3 or mg / L
= 0.001	g / cm^3 or kg / dm^3
= 0.001	mg / mm^3 or mg / μL

milligram per cubic decimetre (mg / dm^3)
Unit of mass per volume

= 0.437	gr / ft^3
= 1 × 10^{-6}	g / cm^3 or kg / dm^3 or mg / mm^3
= 0.001	g / dm^3 or kg / m^3 or mg / cm^3
= 1	g / m^3
= 0.001	oz / ft^3

milligram per cubic metre (mg / m³)
Unit of mass per volume

= 4.37 × 10⁻⁴	gr / ft³
= 0.001	g / m³
= 1000	μg / m³
= 1	μg / L
= 28.32	μg / ft³
= 6.242 × 10⁻⁵	lb / 1000 ft³

milligram per cubic millimetre (mg / mm³)
Unit of mass per volume

= 1	g / cm³ or 1 kg / dm³
= 1000	g / dm³ or kg / m³

milligram per gram (mg / g)
Unit of mass per mass

= 1016.047	g / ton
= 907.1848	g / tn
= 1000	g / t
= 29.166	mg / assay ton
= 35.84	oz / ton
= 32	oz / tn
= 32.666	oz / (troy) ton
= 29.166	oz / (troy) tn
= 2.24	lb / ton
= 2	lb / tn
= 2.722 22	lb / (troy) ton
= 2.430 55	lb / (troy) tn

milligram per inch (mg / in)
Unit of mass per length

= 0.386 089	dyn / cm
= 0.015 432	gr / in
= 3.937 × 10⁻⁴	g / cm
= 0.039 37	kg / km
= 2.204 62 × 10⁻⁴	lb / in

milligram per kilogram (mg / kg)
Unit of mass per mass

= 1.016 407	g / ton
= 0.907 184 8	g / tn
= 1	g / t
= 0.035 84	oz / ton
= 0.032	oz / tn
= 0.002 24	lb / ton
= 0.002	lb / tn

milligram per litre (mg / L)
Unit of mass per volume
(See also mg / dm³)

= 1.603 35 × 10⁻⁴	oz / (UK) gal
= 1.335 13 × 10⁻⁴	oz / (US) gal
= 1	ppm

milligram per millimetre (mg / mm)
Unit of mass per length

= 9.806 65	dyn / cm
= 0.391 982	gr / in
= 0.01	g / cm
= 1	kg / km

milligram per square centimetre (mg / cm^2)
Unit of mass per area

= 0.929	g / ft^2
= 10	g / m^2 or Mg / km^2
= 10 000	mg / m^2
= 89.22	lb / acre
= 2.046	lb / 1000 ft^2
= 25.47	ton / mi^2
= 28.55	tn / mi^2
= 10	t / km^2

milligram per square decimetre day [mg / (dm^2·d)]
Unit of mass per area time

= 0.1	g / (m^2·d)
= 0.004 167	g / (m^2·h)
= 36.524 219	g / (m^2·yr)
= 3.277 × 10^{-4}	oz / (ft^2·d)

milligram per square metre (mg / m^2)
Unit of mass per area

= 0.001	g / m^2 or t / km^2
= 0.0001	mg / cm^2
= 1	kg / km^2
= 0.008 922	lb / acre
= 0.002 854	tn / mi^2

millihenry (mH)
Unit of electric inductance

= 1 × 10^6	aH	(abhenry)
= 1 × 10^3	μH	(microhenry)
= 1 × 10^{-15}	sH	(stathenry)

millilambert (mLa)
Unit of luminance

= 10	asb (apostilb)
= 3.183 099	cd / m^2
= 0.929 04	ft·La or lm / ft^2
= 0.001	lm / cm^2
= 0.295 72	lm / (sr·ft^2)

millilitre (mL)
Unit of capacity

= 0.2816	dr	(UK)
= 0.2706	dr	(US)
= 1	cm^3	
= 16.232	minims	
= 1000	μL	

millimetre (mm)
Unit of length

=	0.039 37	in
=	39.37	mils
=	1×10^3	microns
=	1×10^9	micromicrons
=	1×10^7	Å (angstrom)

millimetre of mercury (mmHg, 0°C)
Unit of pressure

=	$1.333\ 22 \times 10^{-3}$	bar
=	$1.333\ 22 \times 10^3$	dyn / cm²
=	1.3595	gf / cm²
=	0.013 333	N / cm²
=	133.33	Pa
=	0.013 59	tf / m²
=	1	torr

millimetre per second (mm / s)
Unit of velocity or speed

=	11.811	ft / h
=	2.362 21	in / min
=	0.039 37	in / s

millimicron (mμ)
Unit of length

=	1×10^{-7}	cm
=	10	Å (angstrom)
=	3.937×10^{-8}	in
=	1×10^{-9}	m (= 1 nm)
=	1×10^{-3}	μm or micron
=	1×10^{-6}	mm
=	3.937×10^{-5}	mil

million Btu per ton (MBtu / t)
Unit of energy

=	1.163	GJ / t

million electronvolts (MeV)
Unit of energy

=	0.160 219	pJ (picojoule)

million (UK) gallons (Mgal)
Unit of volume or capacity

=	3.685 573	acre ft
=	160 543.6	ft³
=	5946.058	yd³
=	1 200 949	gal (US)
=	4546.090	m³
=	4 546 090	L

million (US) gallons (Mgal)
Unit of volume or capacity

=	3.068 883	acre ft
=	133 680.5	ft³
=	4951.132	yd³
=	832 674.7	gal (UK)
=	3785.412	m³
=	3 785 412	L

million (UK) gallons per day (Mgal / d)
Unit of volume per time
     = 1.858 07 ft^3 / s
     = 4546.09 m^3 / d
     = 52.617   L / s

million (US) gallons per day (Mgal / d)
Unit of volume per time
     = 1.547 23 ft^3 / s
     = 3785.41 m^3 / d
     = 43.8125   L / s

million pounds (avdp) per year (Mlb / a)
Unit of mass per time
     = 1242.67   kg / d (or 1.242 67 Mg / d)
     = 51.5946   kg / h
     = 0.863 24   kg / min
     = 0.014 384   kg / s (or 14.384 g / s)

milli – miscellaneous units			
1 mrad / s	=	13.75	r / d
1 mph	=	10	lm / m^2
"	=	10	lx
1 mT	=	10	Gs
1 mV	=	1×10^5	aV
"	=	1×10^3	μV
"	=	3.334×10^{-6}	Sv

minute, centesimal (...^{c})
Unit of angular measure
     = 0.009   ...° (degree)
     = 0.01   ...^{g} (grade)
     = 0.54   ...' (minute)
     = 0.0001   ...^{L} (quadrant)
     = 1.571×10^{-4} rad (radian)
     = 2.5×10^{-5} ...^{r} (revolution)
     = 32.4   ..." (seconds, sexagesimal)
     = 100   ...^{cc} (seconds, centesimal)

minute, sexagesimal (...')
Unit of angular measure
     = 0.016 666   ...° (degree)
     = 0.018 519   ...^{g} (grade)
     = 1.852×10^{-4} ...^{L} (quadrant)
     = 2.909×10^{-4} rad (radian)
     = 4.630×10^{-5} ...^{r} (revolution)
     = 60   ...' (seconds, sexagesimal)
     = 185.2   ...^{cc} (seconds, centesimal)

minute, mean solar (min)
Unit of time
     = $6.944 444 \times 10^{-4}$ d (mean solar)
     = 0.016 666   h   "   "
     = 60   s   "   "
     = $2.283 11 \times 10^{-5}$ mo (mean calendar)
     = $9.920 64 \times 10^{-5}$ wk   "   "
     = $1.902 39 \times 10^{-6}$ yr (calendar)

month, mean calendar (mo)
Unit of time

=	30.416 66	d	(mean solar)
=	730	h	" "
=	43 800	min	" "
=	2 628 000	s	" "
=	4.345 238	wk	(mean calendar)
=	0.833 333	yr	(calendar)

month	(28 d)	=	672 h	=	40 320 min	=	2 419 200 s
"	(29 d)	=	696 h	=	41 760 min	=	2 505 600 s
"	(30 d)	=	720 h	=	43 200 min	=	2 592 000 s
"	(31 d)	=	744 h	=	44 640 min	=	2 678 400 s

– N –

newton (N)
Unit of force
=	1	kg·m / s^2
=	1 × 10^5	dyn
=	101.97	gf
=	7.2331	pdl
=	1.0197 × 10^{-4}	tf

newton per square centimetre (N / cm^2)
Unit of pressure
=	100	mbar
=	75.1	mmHg (0°C)
=	1.0197	tf / m^2

newton per square metre (N / m^2)
Unit of pressure
=	10	μbar
=	1	Pa

newton metre (N·m)
Unit of bending moment (torque)
=	0.101 972	kgf·m
=	0.737 562	lbf·ft
=	8.850 75	lbf·in
=	27.3704	pdl·ft
=	1	W·s

newton metre per metre (Nm / m)
Unit of bending moment per length
=	0.018 734	lbf·ft / in
=	0.224 809	lbf·in / in

newton second per square metre (N·s / m^2)
Unit of dynamic viscosity
=	1000	cP (centipoise)
=	1000	mN·s / m^2
=	10	P
=	1	Pl (poiseuille)

nit (−)
Unit of luminance
=	6.452 × 10^{-4}	cd / in^2
=	1	cd / m^2
=	1 × 10^{-4}	sb (stilb)

noggin (UK)
Unit of capacity
=	142.1	mL
=	1	gi (gill)
=	0.125	qt

– O –

oersted (Oe)
Unit of magnetic field strength

=	2.021 27	At / in
=	79.5775	A / m
=	1	cgs emu
=	2.998 × 10^{10}	cgs esu
=	1	Gb / cm

ohm (Ω)
Unit of electric resistance

=	1 × 10^9	abohms
=	1	cgs unit of resistance
=	1 × 10^{-6}	megohm
=	1.1126 × 10^{-12}	statohm

Supplementary units		
1 Ω·cm	= 6 015 305	Ω·circ. mil / ft
"	= 6 015 305	Ω·mil·ft
1 Ω·circ. mil / ft	= 1.622 × 10^{-3}	Ω·mm^2 / m
1 Ω·g / m^2	= 5710.95	Ω·lb / mi^2
1 Ω·in	= 1.528 × 10^7	Ω·circ. mil / ft
1 Ω·m^2 / m	= 6.015 × 10^8	Ω·circ. mil / ft
1 Ω·mm^2 / m	= 601.53	Ω·circ. mil / ft

ounce (apoth. or troy oz)
Unit of mass

=	8	dr (apoth.)
=	17.554	dr (avdp)
=	480	gr
=	31.103 486	g
=	20	dwt (pennyweight)
=	24	sc (scrupule)
=	1.097 143	oz (avdp)

ounce (avoirdupois oz)
Unit of mass

=	7.2916	dr (apoth.)
=	16	dr (avdp)
=	437.5	gr
=	28.349 53	g
=	18.229	dwt (pennyweight)
=	21.875	sc (scrupule)
=	2.790 18 × 10^{-5}	ton
=	3.125 00 × 10^{-5}	tn
=	2.834 96 × 10^{-5}	t

ounce (UK) fluid
Unit of capacity

=	28.413	mL or cm^3
=	8	dr
=	0.006 25	gal (UK)
=	0.2	gi (gill)
=	0.960 76	oz (US fl)
=	0.025	qt (UK)

ounce (US) fluid
Unit of capacity

=	29.574	mL or cm^3
=	8	dr
=	0.007 813	gal (US)
=	0.25	gi (gill)
=	1.040 85	oz (UK fl)
=	0.031 25	qt (US)

ounce (avdp) per cubic foot (oz / ft^3)
Unit of mass per volume

=	437.5	gr / ft^3
=	1001.15	mg / dm^3 or g / m^3
=	1.001 15	mg / cm^3 or g / dm^3
=	0.160 54	oz / (UK) gal
=	0.133 68	oz / (US) gal
=	0.0625	lb / ft^3
=	1.6875	lb / yd^3

ounce (avdp) per cubic inch (oz / in^3)
Unit of mass per volume

=	1728	oz / ft^3
=	108	lb / ft^3
=	0.0625	lb / in^3
=	2916	lb / yd^3
=	17.325	lb / (UK) gal
=	14.4375	lb / (US) gal
=	1.308	ton / yd^3
=	1.458	tn / yd^3
=	1.73	t / m^3

ounce (avdp) per (UK) gallon (oz / gal)
Unit of mass per volume

=	2726.6	gr / ft^3
=	6.228 84	oz / ft^3
=	6236.02	g / m^3 or mg / dm^3 or mg / mL
=	6.236 02	g / dm^3 or g / L
=	6.236 02	kg / m^3 or kg / kL
=	6.236 02	mg / cm^3 or mg / mL
=	0.389 41	lb / ft^3
=	10.52	lb / yd^3
=	0.0625	lb / (UK) gal

ounce (avdp) per (US) gallon (oz / gal)
Unit of mass per volume

=	3272.7	gr / ft^3
=	7.480 21	oz / ft^3
=	7489.15	g / m^3 or mg / dm^3 or mg / mL
=	7.489 15	g / dm^3 or g / L
=	7.489 15	kg / m^3 or kg / kL
=	7.489 15	mg / cm^3 or mg / mL
=	0.4675	lb / ft^3
=	12.623	lb / yd^3
=	0.0625	lb / (US) gal

Supplementary units

1 oz (avdp) / in	=	1.116	kg / m
1 oz (UK fl) / s	=	28.413	cm^3 / s
"	=	1.705	L / min
1 oz (US fl) / s	=	29.573	cm^3 / s
"	=	1.775	L / min
1 oz (avdp) / ton	=	27.902	g / t or mg / kg
1 oz (avdp) / tn	=	31.25	g / t or mg / kg
1 oz (apoth.) / ton	=	30.612 25	g / t or mg / kg
1 oz (apoth.) / tn	=	34.2857	g / t or mg / kg
1 ounce-force (ozf)	=	0.278 014	N
"	=	2011	pdl
1 ozf / ft^2	=	305.152	gf / m^2
"	=	2.993	Pa
1 ozf / in^2	=	43 942	gf / m^2
"	=	430.992	Pa
1 ozf·in	=	0.007 061	N·m
"	=	0.167 573	pdl·ft
1 ozf·in^2	=	0.1829	kgf·cm^2

ounce – examples of foreign units

1 onça	–	Brazil	=	28.69	g
1 once	–	Damascus	=	213.5	g
1 once	–	Syria	=	320.5	g
1 onça	–	India	=	28.69	g
1 once	–	Mauritius	=	30.594	g
1 once	–	Seychelles	=	30.594	g
1 once	–	Zanzibar	=	28	g
1 ons	–	Netherlands	=	100	g
1 onza	–	Honduras	=	28.8	g
1 onza	–	Cuba	=	28.75	g
1 onza	–	Philippines	=	28.75	g
1 onza	–	Spain	=	28.75	g
1 onza	–	Argentina	=	28.71	g
1 onza	–	Columbia	=	31.25	g
1 onza	–	Dominican Rep	=	28.35	g
1 onza	–	Honduras	=	28.80	g
1 onza	–	Mexico	=	28.765	g
1 onza	–	Guatemala	=	28.75	g
1 onza	–	Peru	=	28.75	g
1 onza	–	Paraguay	=	28.69	g
1 ounce	–	Pakistan	=	28.35	g

– P –

parsec (pc)
Unit of length in astronomy
= 206 265	AU	(astronomical unit)
= 30.858	Pm	(petametre)
= 3.26	l·y·	(light year)

pascal (Pa)
Unit of pressure
= 1	N / m^2
= 10	dyn / cm^2
= 10	μbar

pascal second (Pa·s)
Unit of dynamic viscosity
= 1000	cP	(centipoise)
= 10	dyn·s / cm^2	
= 0.671 969	lb (mass) / (ft·s)	
= 0.020 885	lbf / (s·ft^2)	
= 1.450 37 × 10^{-4}	lbf / (s·in^2)	

peck (UK)
Unit of volume
= 0.25	bushel
= 2	gal (UK)
= 9.092	dm^3 or L

peck (US)
Unit of volume
= 0.25	bu
= 2	gal (US dry)
= 2.327	gal (US liq.)
= 8.81	dm^3 or L

pennyweight (dwt)
Unit of mass
= 24	gr	
= 1.555	g	
= 0.05	oz	(apoth.)

permeance (perm, 23°C)
Unit of permeable membranes
= 1	gr / (ft^2·h·inHg)
= 57.452	ng / (Pa·s·m^2)

permeance (perm in, 23°C)
Unit of permeable membranes
= 1	gr / (ft^2·h·inHg)
= 1.459 29	ng / (Pa·s·m^2)

phot (ph)
Unit of luminance
= 1	lm / cm^2
= 10 000	lm / m^2 or lx

pica (printer's)
Unit of measurement (size of type)
= 4.217 52	mm
= 12	points

pint (UK liq. pt)
Unit of capacity
= 528.26	cm^3 or mL	
= 0.125	gal	(UK)
= 4	gi	(gill)
= 4	noggins	(UK)

pint (US liq. pt)
Unit of capacity
= 473.176	cm^3 or mL	
= 0.125	gal	(US)
= 16	oz	(US fl)
= 28.875	in^3	

pint (US dry pt)
Unit of volume (dry measure)
= 550.61	cm^3	
= 0.125	gal	(US dry)
= 0.145 46	gal	(US liq.)
= 33.6	in^3	
= 0.0625	peck	
= 0.969	pt	(UK liq.)

pint (UK) per horsepower hour (pt (UK) / hp·h)
Unit of energy (volume consumption)
= 0.762 05	dm^3 / kW·h
= 0.211 281	dm^3 / MJ
= 0.211 281	mm^3 / J

pint (UK) per 1000 barrels (pt (UK) / kbbl)
= 3.574 26	cm^3 / m^3

Miscellaneous units			
point (gems)	=	0.01	carat (metric)
"	=	2	mg
point (paper)	=	0.001	in
"	=	1	mil
point (printer's)	=	0.351 46	mm
"	=	0.083 33	pica
"	=	13.88	mils
poise (viscosity)	=	0.1	Pa·s
"	=	0.1	N·s / m^2
"	=	0.1	Pl
poiseuille (Pl)	=	10	P (poise)
"	=	1	N·s / m^2
"	=	1	Pa·s
pond (p)	=	9.806 65	m·N
"	=	0.071	pdl

pound (apoth or troy lb)
Unit of mass

= 96	dr	
= 210.64	dr	(avdp)
= 5760	gr	
= 373.24	g	
= 12	oz	
= 13.166	oz	(avdp)
= 240	dwt	(pennyweight)
= 288	scrupules	
= 3.733×10^{-4}	Mg or t	(tonne)

pound (avoirdupois lb)
Unit of mass

= 0.01	ctl	(cental)
= 0.125	clove	
= 116.6	dr	(apoth.)
= 256	dr	
= 7000	gr	
= 453.5924	g	
= 0.01	cwt	(hundredweight)
= 14.583	oz	(apoth.)
= 16	oz	
= 291.6	dwt	(pennyweight)
= 1.216	lb	(apoth.)
= 350	sc	(apoth.)
= $4.464\ 29 \times 10^{-4}$	ton	
= 5×10^{-4}	tn	
= $4.535\ 93 \times 10^{-4}$	Mg or t	(tonne)

pound (avdp) of carbon to CO_2 (25°C)
Unit of energy

= 14 550	Btu
= 5.72	hp
= 4.264	kW·h
= 14.518	lb of H_2O evaporated from and at 212°F

pound (avdp) of carbon to CO_2 (25°C) per hour
Unit of energy

= 5.5357	hp (boiler)
= 4.128	kW

pound (avdp) of ice melted (−)
Unit of energy

= 142.5	Btu
= 36.124	kcal
= 4.98×10^{-4}	ton of refrigeration

pound of water (39.2°F)
Unit of mass

= 0.016 019	ft^3
= 27.682	in^3
= 0.10	gal (UK)
= 0.119 83	gal (US)
= 453.592	g or mL

pound of water evaporated from and at 212°F
Unit of energy

=	970.2	Btu
=	0.3813	hp·h
=	1024	kJ
=	0.284 33	kW·h

pound of water raised from 62 to 212°F
Unit of energy

=	150.17	Btu
=	158.4	kJ
=	0.043 973	kW·h

pound of water per second (39.2°F)
Unit of energy

=	0.961 14	ft^3 / min
=	5.986 75	gal (UK) / min
=	7.189 787	gal (US) / min
=	0.10	gal (UK) / s
=	0.119 83	gal (US) / s
=	27.277 78	L / min
=	454.609	mL / s

pound per acre (−)
Unit of mass per area

=	1.121	kg / ha
=	112.1	kg / km^2 or mg / m^2
=	0.2857	ton / mi^2
=	0.318 47	tn / mi^2
=	0.1121	t / km^2

pound per barrel (lb / bbl)
Unit of mass per volume

=	2.853	kg / m^3

pound per cubic foot (lb / ft^3)
Unit of mass per volume

=	16.019	kg / m^3
=	1.245	lb / bu
=	0.160 42	lb / (UK) gal
=	0.133 68	lb / (US) gal
=	0.012 054	ton / yd^3
=	0.0135	tn / yd^3
=	0.016 015	t / m^3

pound per cubic inch (lb / in^3)
Unit of mass per volume

=	27.68	g / cm^3 or kg / dm^3
=	27.648	oz / ft^3
=	1728	lb / ft^3
=	277.2	lb / (UK) gal
=	231	lb / (US) gal
=	20.829	ton / yd^3
=	23.328	tn / yd^3
=	27.6766	t / m^3

pound per cubic yard (lb / yd^3)
Unit of mass per volume
= 0.593 28	kg / m^3	
= 0.5926	oz / ft^3	
= 0.046	lb / bu	(US)
= 0.037 034	lb / ft^3	
= 0.005 947	lb / gal	(UK)
= 0.004 952	lb / gal	(US)
= 0.005 762	lb / gal	(US dry)
= 4.4643	ton / yd^3	
= 5 × 10^{-4}	tn / yd^3	
= 1.933 × 10^{-4}	t / m^3	

pound per day (lb / d)
Unit of mass per time
= 0.0189	kg / h
= 0.6667	oz / h
= 0.041 66	lb / h
= 1.861 × 10^{-5}	ton / h
= 2.084 × 10^{-5}	tn / h
= 1.85 × 10^{-9}	t / h

pound per foot (lb / ft)
Unit of mass per time
= 229.7	gr / cm
= 583.33	gr / in
= 14.882	g / cm
= 37.8	g / in
= 1.4882	kg / m
= 84 480	oz / mi
= 1.4882	t / km

pound per foot second [lb / (ft·s)]
Unit of dynamic viscosity
= 1488.2	cP	(centipoise)
= 1.4882	Pa·s	
= 14.882	g / (cm·s)	
= 14.882	P	(poise)
= 1	pdl·s / ft^2	

pound per (UK) gallon (lb / gal)
Unit of mass per volume
= 0.099 776 4	g / cm^3
= 99.7764	g / dm^3 or kg / m^3
= 2.825 354	kg / ft^3
= 76.284 55	kg / yd^3
= 99.661	oz / ft^3
= 2691	oz / yd^3
= 168.179	lb / yd^3
= 0.075 08	ton / yd^3
= 0.084 089	tn / yd^3
= 0.099 776	t / m^3

pound per (US) gallon (lb / gal)
Unit of mass per volume

=	0.119 826	g / cm^3
=	119.826	g / dm^3 or kg / m^3
=	3.393 106	kg / ft^3
=	91.613 88	kg / yd^3
=	119.688	oz / ft^3
=	3231.6	oz / yd^3
=	201.974	lb / yd^3
=	0.090 167	ton / yd^3
=	0.100 987	tn / yd^3
=	0.119 826	t / yd^3

pound per horsepower hour (lb / hp·h)

=	0.169	kg / kJ or mg / J
=	0.6083	kg / kW·h

pound per hour (lb / h)
Unit of mass per time

=	10.886	kg / d
=	0.125 998	g / s
=	384	oz / d
=	2.777 × 10^{-4}	lb / s
=	0.010 714	ton / d
=	0.012	tn / d
=	0.010 886	t / d

pound per inch (lb / in)
Unit of mass per length

=	84 000	gr / ft
=	178.6	g / cm
=	6.3	oz / cm
=	63 360	lb / mi
=	28.286	ton / mi
=	31.68	tn / mi
=	17.857 97	t / km
=	28.739 92	t / mi

pound per mile (lb / mi)
Unit of mass per length or distance

=	0.281 249	kg / km
=	0.003 03	oz / ft
=	2.773 98 × 10^{-4}	ton / km
=	4.464 × 10^{-4}	ton / mi
=	3.106 85 × 10^{-4}	tn / km
=	5 × 10^{-4}	tn / mi
=	2.818 49 × 10^{-4}	t / km
=	4.535 92 × 10^{-4}	t / mi

pound per minute (lb / min)
Unit of mass per time

=	27.2156	kg / h
=	0.03	tn / h
=	0.027 216	t / h

pound per second (lb / s)
Unit of mass per time
=	1632.94	kg / h
=	1 382 400	oz / d
=	57 600	oz / h
=	960	oz / min
=	38.573	ton / d
=	43.2	tn / d
=	39.191	t / d

pound per square foot (lb / ft^2)
Unit of mass per area
=	0.488 243	g / cm^2
=	4.882 43	kg / m^2
=	0.111	oz / in^2

Supplementary units			
lb / ton	=	446.429	g / t or mg / kg
lb / tn	=	500	g / t or mg / kg
lb (troy) / ton	=	367.347	g / t or mg / kg
lb (troy) / tn	=	411.429	g / t or mg / kg

pound-force (lbf)
Unit of force
=	444.822	dyn	(dyne)
=	453.592	gf	(gram-force)
=	32.174	pdl	(poundal)
=	5×10^{-4}	tnf	(short ton-force)
=	4.537×10^{-4}	tf	(tonne-force)

pound-force foot (lbf·ft)
Unit of torque
=	1.3582	N·m	(newton-metre)
=	12	lbf·in	
=	4.4643×10^{-4}	tonf·ft	
=	5×10^{-4}	tnf·ft	
=	4.5347×10^{-4}	tf·ft	

pound-force inch (lbf·in)
Unit of bending moment (torque)
=	0.112 985	N·m
=	2.681 17	pdl·ft
=	0.083 33	lbf·ft
=	3.7203×10^{-5}	tonf·ft

pound-force inch per inch (lbf·in / in)
Unit of torque per length
=	4.448 22	N·m / m

pound-force per foot (lbf / ft)
Unit of force per length
=	14.5939	N / m

pound-force per square foot (lbf / ft²)
Unit of pressure

= 4.788 × 10⁻⁴	bar
= 478.8	dyn / cm²
= 13.096	ft of air (60°F, 1 atm)
= 0.488 242	gf / cm²
= 0.047 881	kN / m² or kPa
= 0.111	ozf / in²
= 5 × 10⁻⁴	tnf / ft²

pound-force per square inch (lbf / in² or psi)
Unit of pressure

= 0.068 948	bar
= 5.712	cmHg (0°C)
= 70.309	cmH₂O (4°C)
= 68 948	dyn / cm²
= 1885.8	ft of air (60°F, 1 atm)
= 2.309	ft of water (60°F)
= 70.307	gf / cm²
= 6.894 76	kN / m² or kPa
= 51.72	mmHg (0°C)
= 2304	oz / ft²
= 4633	pdl / ft²
= 0.072	tnf / ft²
= 5 × 10⁻⁴	tnf / in²
= 0.703 267	tf / m²

pound-force second per square inch (lbf·s / in²)
Unit of dynamic viscosity

= 6.894 76	kPa·s
= 68 947.6	P (poise)

Supplementary units		
pound-mole (lb·mol)	= 0.453 592	kmol
lb·mol / (UK) gal	= 99.776 34	kmol / m³
lb·mol / (US) gal	= 119.826	kmol / m³
lb·mol (perfect gas)	= 359	ft³ (0°C, 1 atm)
"	= 379	ft³ (15.5°C, 1 atm)
"	= 392	ft³ (25°C, 1 atm)

poundal (pdl)
Unif of force

= 13 826	dyn
= 14.098	gf
= 0.138 25	N
= 0.031	lbf
= 0.014	kgf
= 1.554 × 10⁻⁵	tnf
= 1.410 × 10⁻⁵	tf

poundal per cubic inch (pdl / in^3)
Unit of force per volume

= 0.860 318	gf / cm^3
= 0.031 08	lbf / in^3
= 1.488 164	Pa
= 0.004 297	kgf·m
= 1.3875 $\times$ 10^{-5}	tnf·ft

poundal foot (pdl·ft)
Unit of moment of force

= 0.372 971	lbf·in
= 0.042 140	N·m

poundal second per square foot (pdl·s / ft^2)
Unif of dynamic viscosity

= 1.4882	N·s / m^2
= 1	lbf·ft / s^2

– Q –

quad (–)
Unit of energy
= 1.055 056	EJ	(exajoule)	
= 293.071	TW·h	(terawatt-hour)	

quadrant (...^{L}) or right angle
Unit of angular measure
= 90	...°	(degree)	
= 100	...^{g}	(grade)	
= 5400	...$'$	(minute)	
= 1.570 796	rad	(radian)	
= 0.25	...^{r}	(revolution)	
= 324 000	...$''$	(second)	

Quart (UK qt)
Unit of capacity and volume
= 1136.52	cm^3 or mL	
= 69.355	in^3	
= 0.25	gal	
= 0.300 24	gal	(US)
= 1.136 52	dm^3 or L	
= 40	oz	
= 1.032 06	qt	(US dry)
= 1.200 95	qt	(US liq.)

quart (US qt)
Unit of capacity
= 946.353	cm^3 or mL	
= 57.74	in^3	
= 0.25	gal	
= 0.214 85	gal	(US dry)
= 32	oz	
= 0.832 68	qt	(UK liq.)
= 0.859 37	qt	(US dry)

quart (US qt dry)
Unit of volume
= 1101.23	cm^3	
= 67.201	in^3	
= 0.25	gal	(US dry)
= 0.290 91	gal	(US liq.)
= 1.101 23	dm^3 or L	
= 0.968 94	qt	(UK)
= 1.163 85	qt	(US liq.)

quarter (UK)
Unit of length
= 22.86	cm
= 1	span
= 9	in

quarter (UK, long)
Unit of mass
= 12.700 586	kg	
= 28	lb	(avdp)

quarter (UK, short)
Unit of mass
= 11.3399	kg	
= 25	lb	(avdp)

quarter (US, long)
Unit of mass
= 254.011 727	kg	
= 560	lb	(avdp)
= 0.25	ton	(long)

quarter (US, short)
Unit of mass
= 226.796 185	kg	
= 500	lb	(avdp)
= 0.25	tn	(short)

quartern (UK liq.)
Unit of capacity
= 142.065	mL or cm^3	
= 1	gill	(UK)
= 5	oz	(UK fl)

quartern (UK dry)
Unit of volume
= 0.5	gal	(UK)
= 2.272 98	L	
= 0.25	peck (UK)	

quintal (metric)
Unit of mass
= 100 000	g	
= 1.968 413	cwt	(long)
= 2.204 622 6	cwt	(short)
= 100	kg	
= 220.462 26	lb	(avdp)

quintal – examples of foreign units					
1 quintal – UK (long)	=	112	lb	= 50.802 35	kg
" – US (short)	=	100	lb	= 45.359 24	kg
1 quintal – Spain	=	101.4 lb		= 46	kg
" – Costa Rica	=	101.4 lb		= 46	kg
" – Guatemala	=	101.4 lb		= 46	kg
" – Venezuela	=	101.4 lb		= 46	kg
" – Cuba	=	101.4 lb		= 46	kg
" – Honduras	=	101.4 lb		= 46	kg
" – Brazil	=	129.5 lb		= 58.75	kg
" – Argentina	=	101.4 lb		= 46	kg
" – Br. Hond.	=	100 lb		= 45.359	kg
" – Columbia	=	110.2 lb		= 50	kg
" – Mexico	=	101.4 lb		= 46.03	kg
" – Paraguay	=	101.2 lb		= 45.9	kg
" – El Salvador	=	101.4 lb		= 46	kg
" – Peru	=	101.4 lb		= 46	kg
" – Chile	=	101.4 lb		= 46	kg
" – Dom. Rep.	=	100 lb		= 45.359	kg
" – Philippines	=	101.4 lb		= 46	kg

– R –

rad (rd) – radiology
Unit of absorbed dose of radiation
=	0.01	Gy	(gray)
=	1.19	rep	

radian (rad)
Unit of angular measure
=	57.295 779	...°	(degree) or 57°17′45″
=	63.661 977	...g	(grade) or 63g 66′17″
=	3437.747	...′	(minute)
=	0.636 62	..ᴸ	(quadrant)
=	0.159 155	...r	(revolution)
=	206 264.8	...″	(second)

radian per centimetre (rad / cm)
Unit of angular measure
=	57.295 779	...° / cm
=	1746.375	...° / ft
=	145.532	...° / in
=	3437.747	...′ / cm

radian per hour (rad / h)
Unit of angular velocity
=	0.015 916	...° / s
=	0.017 684	...g / s
=	2.7778×10^{-4}	rad / s
=	4.4211×10^{-5}	...r / s

radian per minute (rad / min)
Unit of angular velocity
=	0.954 929	...° / s
=	1.061 033	...g / s
=	0.016 667	rad / s
=	0.002 653	...r / s

radian per second (rad / s)
Unit of angular velocity
=	57.295 779	...° / s
=	63.661 977	...g / s
=	13 750.987	...r / d
=	9.549 296	...r / min
=	0.159 155	...r / s

radian per second squared (rad / s²)
Unit of angular acceleration
=	572.958	...r / min²
=	9.549 296	...r / (min·s)
=	0.159 155	...r / s²

rayl (–)
Unit of specific acoustical impedence
=	1	bar / (cm·s)
=	10	N·s / m³

register ton (–)
Unit of volume
=	2.831 685	m³

rem (−) − radiology
Unit of dose equivalent
= 0.01	J / kg or Sv	(sievert)
= 10	mSv	

revolution (...^{r})
Unit of angular measure
= 360	...°	(degree)
= 400	...^{g}	(grade)
= 21 600	...'	(minute)
= 4	...^{L}	(quadrant)
= 6.283 185	rad	(radian)
= 1 296 000	...″	(second)

revolution per day (...^{r} / d)
Unit of angular velocity
= 4.166 × 10^{-3}	...° / s
= 4.629 × 10^{-3}	...^{g} / s
= 7.272 × 10^{-5}	rad / s
= 1.157 × 10^{-5}	...^{r} / s

revolution per hour (...^{r} / h)
Unit of angular velocity
= 0.1	...° / s
= 0.111 11	...^{g} / s
= 0.001 745 33	rad / s
= 2.777 78 × 10^{-4}	...^{r} / s

revolution per minute (...^{r} / min)
Unit of angular velocity
= 6	...° / s
= 6.666	...^{g} / s
= 0.104 719	rad / s
= 0.016 666	...^{r} / s

revolution per minute squared (...^{r} / min^2)
Unit of angular acceleration
= 1.7453 × 10^{-3}	rad / s^2
= 0.016 666	...^{r} / (min·s)
= 2.7778 × 10^{-4}	...^{r} / s^2

revolution per second (...^{r} / s)
Unit of angular velocity
= 360	...° / s
= 400	...^{g} / s
= 6.283 185	rad / s

revolution per second squared (...^{r} / s^2)
Unit of angular acceleration
= 6.283 185	rad / s^2
= 3600	rad / min^2
= 60	...^{r} / (min·s)

rhe (−)
Unit of dynamic viscosity
= 10	m^2 / (N·s)
= 1	1 / P or poise^{-1}

rod, pole or perch (–)
Unit of length
=	16.5	ft
=	0.025	furlong
=	5.0292	m

roentgen (R) – radiology
Unit of exposure
=	2.58×10^{-4}	C / kg

rood (UK)
Unit of area
=	0.25	acre
=	10 890	ft^2
=	1011.714	m^2
=	40	sq·rods
=	1210	yd^2

rutherford (Rd)
Unit of radioactivity
=	1×10^{-6}	s^{-1} (reciprocal second)

rydberg (Ry)
Unit of energy used in atomic physics
=	2.4253×10^{-32}	g	(gram)
=	2.1797×10^{-18}	J	(joule)
=	2.1797×10^{-11}	erg	(erg)
=	1.4606×10^{-8}	u	(atomic mass unit)
=	1.3606×10	eV	(electronvolt)
=	1.0974×10^5	cm^{-1}	(reciprocal centimetre)
=	1.5790×10^5	K	(kelvin)
=	3.2898×10^{15}	s^{-1}	(reciprocal second)

– S –

scruple (sc) – apoth. or troy
Unit of mass
= 20	gr
= 1.296	g

scruple (UK fl)
Unit of capacity
= 0.333 33	dr	(fl)
= 20	minims	
= 0.041 66	oz	(fl)

seam (UK)
Unit of volume
= 8	bushels	(UK)
= 64	gal	(UK)
= 290.95	dm^3 or L	

second^{-1} (s^{-1})
Unit of energy used in atomic physics
= 7.3720 × 10^{-48}	g	(gram)
= 6.6256 × 10^{-34}	J	(joule)
= 6.6256 × 10^{-27}	erg	(erg)
= 4.4398 × 10^{-24}	u	(atomic mass unit)
= 3.0397 × 10^{-16}	Ry	(rydberg)
= 4.1356 × 10^{-15}	eV	(electronvolt)
= 3.3356 × 10^{-11}	cm^{-1}	(reciprocal centimetre)
= 4.7993 × 10^{-11}	K	(kelvin)

second, centesimal (...^{cc})
Unit of angular measure
= 9 × 10^{-5}	...°	(degree)
= 1 × 10^{-4}	...^{g}	(grade)
= 1.571 × 10^{-6}	rad	(radian)

second, sexagesimal (...′)
Unit of angular measure
= 2.7778 × 10^{-4}	...°	(degree)
= 3.0864 × 10^{-4}	...^{g}	(grade)
= 1.6666 × 10^{-2}	...′	(minute)
= 3.0861 × 10^{-6}	...^{L}	(quadrant)
= 4.8480 × 10^{-6}	rad	(radian)
= 7.7161 × 10^{-7}	...^{r}	(revolution)

second, mean solar (...^{s})
Base unit of time
= 1.157 407 × 10^{-5}	d	(mean solar)
= 2.777 778 × 10^{-4}	h	" "
= 1.666 667 × 10^{-2}	min	" "
= 3.805 175 × 10^{-7}	mo	(mean calendar)
= 1.653 439 × 10^{-6}	wk	" "
= 3.170 979 × 10^{-8}	yr	(calendar)
= 3.168 754 × 10^{-8}	yr	(sideral)
= 3.168 877 × 10^{-8}	yr	(tropical)

section (–)
Unit of area
    = 640   acres
    = 2.589 988 km^2
    = 1 mi^2

siemens (S)
Unit of conductance
    = 1   A / V
    = 1 $1 / \Omega$ (reciprocal ohm)

sievert (Sv) – radiology
Unit of dose equivalent
    = 1   J / kg

sign (–)
Unit of angular measure
    = 30   ...°   (degree)
    = 0.083 333   ...^{r} (revolution)

slug (–)
Unit of mass
    = 32.174   lb
    = 14.5939   kg

slug per cubic foot (–)
Unit of density
    = 32.174 lb / ft^3
    = 515.378 kg / m^3

slug per foot second (–)
Unit of dynamic viscosity
    = 47.88   Pa·s
    = 1 $lb·s / ft^2$

spherical right angle (–)
Unit of angular measure
    = 0.25   hemisphere
    = 0.125   sphere
    = 1.5708   sr   (steradian)

square arpent (arp^2)
Unit of area
    = 36 000 ft^2
    = 3418.85 m^2

square centimetre (cm^2)
Unit of area
    = 0.197 352 52   circ. in
    = 127.323 95   circ. mm
    = 197 352.52   circ. mils
    = 155 001   sq. mils
    = 0.155 in^2
    = 100 mm^2

square centimetre per dyne (cm^2 / dyn)
Unit of area per force

=	980.665	cm^2 / gf
=	68 948	in^2 / lbf
=	10	m^2 / N
=	10	Pa^{-1} (reciprocal pascal)

Supplementary units			
cm^2 / erg	=	1000	m^2 / J
cm^2 / kgf	=	1.0197 × 10^{-5}	m^2 / N
"	=	1.0197 × 10^{-5}	Pa^{-1}
cm^2 / (sr·erg)	=	1000	m^2 / (sr·J)

square centimetre per second (cm^2 / s)
Unit of kinematic viscosity

=	1	St (stokes)
=	0.016 018	P·ft^3 / lb
=	0.061 024	P·in^3 / g
=	1	P·cm^3 / g
=	86 376	L / (cm·d)
=	86 400	cm^2 / d
=	0.36	m^2 / h

square chain (ch^2) – surveyor or Gunter's
Unit of area

=	0.1	acre
=	4356	ft^2
=	10 000	li^2 (sq. link)
=	404.686	m^2
=	16	rod^2 (sq. rod)
=	484	yd^2

square chain (ch^2) – engineer or Ramden's
Unit of area

=	0.229 568	acre
=	10 000	ft^2
=	10 000	li^2
=	929.031	m^2
=	36.731	rod^2
=	1111.1	yd^2

square decimetre (dm^2)
Unit of area

=	100	cm^2
=	0.01	m^2
=	15.5	in^2

square foot (ft^2)
Unit of area

=	929.031	cm^2
=	0.092 903	m^2
=	0.111	yd^2

square foot per hour (ft^2 / h)
Unit of area per time

=	22 296.73	cm^2 / d
=	0.258 064	cm^2 / s

Supplementary units			
ft^2 / min	=	1 337 904	cm^2 / d
"	=	24	in^2 / s
ft^2 / lb	=	2.048 162	cm^2 / g
ft^2 / s	=	929.03	cm^2 / s
"	=	80 268 227	cm^2 / d
"	=	92.903	mm^2 / s
ft^2 / in^3	=	5669.3	m^2 / m^3
ft$^2 \cdot$lb / s^2	=	0.042 140	J
ft^2 / lbf	=	0.002 008	cm^2 / dyn

square hectometre (hm^2)
Unit of area

=	100	a (are)
=	1	ha (hectare)
=	10 000	m^2
=	0.01	km^2
=	11 959.9	yd^2

square inch (in^2)
Unit of area

=	821.443	circ. mm
=	1 273 239.5	circ. mils
=	6.4516	cm^2
=	645.16	mm^2
=	1 000 000	sq·mils

square inch per pound (in^2 / lb)
Unit of area per mass

=	14.223 43	cm^2 / kg

square inch per second (in^2 / s)
Unit of kinematic viscosity

=	6.4516	cm^2 / s
=	22 225.7	cm^2 / h
=	645.16	mm^2 / s
=	0.416 66	ft^2 / min
=	25	ft^2 / h

square kilometre (km^2)
Unit of area

=	0.386 102 16	mi^2
=	247.1054	acres
=	1000	ha
=	1 000 000	m^2
=	1 195 990	yd^2

square link (li^2) – surveyor or Gunter's
Unif of area
=	404.685	cm^2
=	0.4356	ft^2
=	0.0001	sq. chain (Gunter's)
=	62.7264	in^2

square link (li^2) – engineer or Ramden's
Unit of area
=	929.031	cm^2
=	1	ft^2
=	0.01	sq. chain (Ramden's)
=	144	in^2

square metre (m^2)
Unit of area
=	0.01	a (are)
=	1	ca (centiare)
=	10.763 91	ft^2
=	1550.003	in^2
=	1.195 99	yd^2

square mil (mil^2)
Unit of area
=	1.273 24	circ. mil
=	8.2145 $\times$ 10^{-4}	circ. mm
=	6.4516 $\times$ 10^{-4}	mm^2
=	1 $\times$ 10^{-6}	in^2

square mile (mi^2)
Unit of area
=	640	acres
=	259	ha
=	2.59	km^2
=	3 097 600	yd^2
=	27 878 400	ft^2

square millimetre (mm^2)
Unit of area
=	0.01	cm^2
=	1.55 $\times$ 10^{-3}	in^2
=	1.273 24	circ. mm
=	1973.525	circ. mils
=	1 $\times$ 10^{-6}	m^2
=	1 $\times$ 10^{-8}	a (are)
=	1 $\times$ 10^{-10}	ha

square millimetre per second (mm^2 / s)
Unit of kinematic viscosity
=	1.076 391 $\times$ 10^{-5}	ft^2 / s
=	1.550 $\times$ 10^{-3}	in^2 / s
=	3.875 $\times$ 10^{-2}	ft^2 / h
=	1	cSt (centistokes)

Supplementary units			
mm^2 / kg	=	1.574 876	in^2 / ton
"	=	1.406 139	in^2 / tn
mm^2 / kgf	=	1.02 × 10^{-8}	cm^2 / dyn
"	=	7.03 × 10^{-3}	in^2 / lbf
"	=	0.001	m^2 / tf

square rod (rod^2)
Unit of area

=	272.5	ft^2
=	25.293	m^2
=	30.25	yd^2

square yard (yd^2)

=	8361.274	cm^2
=	1296	in^2
=	0.836 128	m^2
=	2.066 116 × 10^{-4}	acre
=	8.361 274 × 10^{-5}	ha

Standard substance density units			
1 std ft^3 (60°F, 1 atm)	=	1.1953 × 10^{-3}	kmol
1 std ft^3 / bbl (60°F, 1 atm)	=	7.5182 × 10^{-3}	kmol / m^3
1 std m^3 (0°C, 1 atm)	=	4.4616 × 10^{-2}	kmol
1 std m^3 (15°C, 1 atm)	=	4.2293 × 10^{-2}	kmol

statampere (sA)
Unit of electric current

=	3.335 × 10^{-11}	aA	(abampere)
=	3.335 × 10^{-10}	A	(ampere)
=	0.333 564	nA	(nanoampere)
=	333.564	pA	(picoampere)

statcoulomb (sC)
Unit of electric charge

=	3.335 × 10^{-11}	aC	
=	3.335 × 10^{-10}	C	
=	0.333 564	nC	
=	333.564	pC	
=	1	Fr	(franklin)

statfarad (sF)
Unit of electric capacitance

=	1.112 65 × 10^{-21}	aF
=	1.112 65 × 10^{-12}	F
=	1.112 65	pF

stathenry (sH)
Unit of electric inductance

=	8.987 59 × 10^{20}	aH
=	8.987 59 × 10^{11}	H
=	0.898 759	TH (terahenry)

statmho (−)

=	1.112 65	pS (picosiemens)

statohm (sΩ)
Unit of electric resistance

= 8.987 × 10²⁰	aΩ	(abohm)
= 8.987 × 10¹¹	Ω	(ohm)
= 898.7	GΩ	(gigaohm)
= 0.8987	TΩ	(teraohm)

statvolt (sV)
Unit of electric potential

= 2.997 × 10¹⁰	aV	(abvolt)
= 299.79	V	

sthène (sn)
Unit of force

= 1	t·m / s²
= 1 × 10⁸	dyn
= 1000	N

steradian (sr)
Unit of measure of solid angle

= 3282.806	square degrees
= 4052.847	square grades
= 0.159 155	hemisphere
= 0.079 577 5	solid angle
= 0.079 577 5	entire space
= 0.079 577 5	sphere
= 0.636 619 8	spherical quadrant

stilb (sb)
Unit of luminance

= 1	cd / cm²
= 10 000	cd / m²
= 2918.6	ft·La
= 3.1416	La
= 10 000	nits

stokes (St)
Unit of kinematic viscosity

= 1	cm² / s
= 1	P·cm³ / g
= 0.016 018	P·ft³ / lb
= 0.061 023	P·in³ / g

stone (UK)
Unit of mass

= 6.3503	kg
= 14	lb

strike (UK)
Unit of volume

= 2	bushels (UK)
= 72.736	dm³ or L
= 0.666	sack
= 0.25	seam

– T –

tesla (T)
Unit of magnetism and magnetic flux density

=	1	Wb / m^2
=	10 000	Gs
=	3.335 × 10^{-7}	cgs esu
=	64 516	lines / in^2

therm (–)
Unit of energy

=	100 000	Btu
=	29.308	kW·h
=	105.510	MJ
=	25.22	th (thermie)

Supplementary units		
therm / ft^3	= 3725.9	MJ / m^3
therm / (UK) gal	= 622 884	Btu / ft^3
"	= 23 208	MJ / m^3
"	= 23 208	kJ / L
"	= 6.447	kW·h / L
therm / (US) gal	= 748 052	Btu / ft^3
"	= 27 872	MJ / m^3
"	= 27 872	kJ / L
"	= 7.742 12	kW·h / L
therm / tn	= 116.3	MJ / t

thermie (th)
Unit of energy

=	4.185	MJ
=	1.163	kW·h
=	1000	kcal (15°C)

thermie per litre (th / L)

=	112 332	Btu / ft^3
=	4185.5	J / mL or kJ / L
=	0.180 342	therm / (UK) gal
=	0.216 172	therm / (US) gal

ton (ton)
Unit of mass (long ton)

=	2240	lb (avdp)
=	1016.047	kg
=	1.12	tn (short ton)
=	1.016 047	Mg or t

ton per cubic yard (ton / yd^3)
Unit of density or concentration

=	1.328 94	g / cm^3
=	1327.4	oz / ft^3
=	13.31	lb / (UK) gal
=	11.083	lb / (US) gal
=	82.962	lb / ft^3
=	1.12	tn / yd^3
=	1.016 047	t / m^3

ton per mile (ton / mi)
Unit of mass per length
=	0.631 342	kg / m
=	1.272 73	lb / yd
=	0.035 353	lb / in

Supplementary units			
ton / min	=	16.394 12	kg / s
ton / mi^2	=	392.298	kg / km^2
"	=	392.298	mg / m^2
"	=	3.5	lb / acre
ton / 1000 yd	=	1.111	kg / m
"	=	2.224	lb / yd
"	=	1.76	ton / mi
ton / yr	=	32.219	mg / s
ton-force	=	9.964 02	kN
tonf·ft	=	3.037	kN·m
tonf / ft^2	=	1.059	atm
"	=	1.0725	bar
"	=	107.252	kN / m^2
"	=	107.252	kPa
"	=	2240	lbf / ft^2
"	=	15.555	lbf / in^2
"	=	72 070	pdl / ft^2
tonf / in^2	=	15.444	MN / m^2
"	=	15.444	MPa
"	=	15.444	N / mm^2

ton (tn)
Unit of mass (short ton)
=	2000	lb (avdp)
=	907.185	kg
=	0.892 857	ton (long)
=	0.907 186	Mg or t (tonne)

ton per cubic foot (tn / ft^3)
Unit of mass per volume or density
=	32.037	g / cm^3 or kg / dm^3
=	32 037	kg / m^3
=	1.158	lb / in^3
=	54 000	lb / yd^3
=	321.07	lb / gal (UK)
=	267.361	lb / gal (US)

ton per cubic yard (tn / yd^3)
Unit of density
=	1.186 56	g / cm^3
=	1186.56	kg / m^3
=	1.1852	oz / ft^3
=	11.892	lb / gal (UK)
=	9.902	lb / gal (US)
=	74.075	lb / ft^3
=	0.892 857	tn / yd^3
=	1.186 56	t / m^3

ton per day (tn / d)
Unit of mass per unit time

=	0.0105	kg / s
=	83.333	lb / h
=	1.388	lb / min
=	0.023 148	lb / s

ton per hour (tn / h)
Unit of mass per unit time

=	0.2515	kg / s
=	48 000	lb / d
=	33.333	lb / min
=	0.555	lb / s

ton per minute (tn / min)
Unit of mass per unit time

=	15.119	kg / s
=	2 880 000	lb / d
=	120 000	lb / h
=	33.333	lb / s

ton of water per day (tnH$_2$0 / d)
Unit of flow rate

=	1.133 62	ft^3 / h
=	630	mL / min
=	0.138 612	gal / min (UK)
=	0.1666	gal / min (US)
=	909.2	L / d
=	37.88	L / h
=	0.6306	L / min

ton-force (tnf)
Unit of force

=	907.184	kgf
=	8.8964	kN
=	0.907 184	tf
=	2000	lbf
=	64 348.2	pdl

ton-force foot (tnf·ft)
Unit of force per length

=	2.711 64	kN·m

ton-force per square foot (tnf / ft^2)
Unit of pressure

=	0.9451	atm
=	0.9576	bar
=	976.5	gf / cm^2
=	28.278	inHg (0°C)
=	384.45	inH$_2$0 (4°C)
=	718.3	mmHg or torr (0°C)
=	13.888	lbf / in^2 (psi)
=	9.764 86	tf / m^2
=	95.760	kN / m^2 or kPa

ton-force per square inch (tnf / in^2)
Unit of pressure

=	136.092	atm
=	1.406 14	kgf / mm^2
=	13.789 52	MN / m^2 or MPa
=	13.789 52	N / mm^2

tonne (t)
Unit of mass (metric ton)

=	1000	kg	
=	1	Mg	
=	32 151	oz	(apoth.)
=	35 274	oz	(avdp)
=	2679.2	lb	(apoth.)
=	2204.62	lb	(avdp)
=	0.984 205	ton	(long)
=	1.102 31	tn	(short)

tonne per cubic metre (t / m^3)
Unit of density or concentration

=	1	g / cm^3 or kg / dm^3	
=	1	mg / mm^3 or Mg / m^3	
=	998.848	oz / ft^3	
=	10.02	lb / gal	(UK)
=	8.3454	lb / gal	(US)
=	62.428	lb / ft^3	
=	0.752 239	ton / yd^3	
=	0.842 778	tn / yd^3	

tonne-force (tf)
Unit of force

=	1000	kgf
=	9806.65	N
=	2204.6	lbf
=	0.983 928	tonf
=	1.1023	tnf

tonne per square metre (t / m^2)
Unit of pressure

=	98 066.5	dyn / cm^2
=	100	gf / cm^2
=	39.37	in of H$_2$0 (4°C)
=	73.55	mmHg (0°C)
=	0.980 665	N / cm^2
=	9806.65	N / m^2 or Pa

	Supplementary units		
tn (register)	=	100	ft³
"	=	2.831 684	m³
tn (refrigeration)	=	12 000	Btu / h
"	=	3.517	kW
"	=	37.97	kg / h (ice melted)
"	=	83.7	lb / h (ice melted)
tn (shipping)	=	40	ft³
"	=	1.132 67	m³
tn (nuclear eq. of TNT, calculated)	=	4.2	GJ (gigajoule)

township (–)
Unit of area

=	23 040	acres
=	36	sections
=	36	mi²
=	93.24	km²

tun (–)
Unit of volume

=	209.834	gal (UK)
=	252	gal (US)
=	4	hogsheads

– U –

unit pole (–)
Unit of magnetic flux

=	12.57	Mx (maxwell)
=	1	cgs emu
=	0.125 663	μWb (microweber)
=	$3.335\ 64 \times 10^{-11}$	cgs esu

unit per henry (1 / H)
Unit of inductance

=	1×10^{-8}	A / line
=	$1.256\ 64 \times 10^{-11}$	Gb / Mx (gilbert per maxwell)
=	1	A / Wb

– V –

volt (V)
Unit of electromotive force

= 1×10^8	aV (abvolt)
= 3.335×10^{-3}	sV (statvolt)
= 1	W / A

volt per centimetre (V / cm)
Unit of electric field strength

= 1×10^8	μV / m
= 1×10^5	mV / m
= 2.54×10^{-3}	V / mil
= 0.1	V / mm

volt per mil (V / mil)
Unit of electric field strength

= 3.937×10^{10}	aV / cm
= 0.3937	kV / cm
= 3.937×10^7	mV / m
= 1.313 24	sV / cm
= 393.7	V / cm
= 1000	V / in
= 39.37	V / mm

Supplementary units		
V / °C	= 1	J / (C·°C)
V / mm	= 1×10^9	aV / cm
"	= 1	kV / m
"	= 1×10^9	μV / m
V / C	= 1	J (joule)
V·A	= 1	W (watt)
V / A	= 1	Ω (ohm)
V·s	= 1	Wb (weber)
V·s / A	= 1	H (henry)
V·s / m^2	= 1	T (tesla)

– W –

watt (W)
Unit of power

=	3.4122	Btu$_{(IT)}$ / h
=	860	cal$_{(IT)}$ / h
=	1 × 10^7	erg / s
=	44.254	ft·lbf / min
=	1423.8	ft·pdl / min
=	1	J / s
=	35.528	L·atm / h
=	680	lm (at 5550 Å)

watt-hour (W·h)
Unit of energy

=	3600	J
=	3.414	Btu
=	860	cal

Supplementary units		
W / (cm·°C)	= 100	W / (m·K)
"	= 57.8	Btu / (ft·h·°F)
W / cm^2	= 3170	Btu / (ft^2·h)
"	= 8598.5	kcal / (m^2·h·°C)
W / (cm^2·K)	= 1761.1	Btu / (ft^2·h·°F)
"	= 8598.5	kcal / (m^2·h·°C)
W / (m·K)	= 0.578	Btu$_{(IT)}$ / (h·ft^2) (°F / ft)
"	= 6.934	Btu$_{(IT)}$ / (h·ft^2) (°F / in)
W / m^2	= 0.317	Btu$_{(IT)}$ / (h·ft^2)
W / (m^2·K)	= 0.176 11	Btu$_{(IT)}$ / (h·ft^2·°F)

weber (Wb)
Unit of magnetism and magnetic flux

=	1	V·s
=	1 × 10^8	Mx
=	1 × 10^8	lines
=	1 × 10^8	cgs units of induction flux
=	1 × 10^8	cgs emu of induction flux

weber per square centimetre (Wb / cm^2)
Unit of magnetic flux density

=	1 × 10^8	Gs (gauss)
=	1 × 10^8	lines / cm^2
=	1 × 10^8	Mx / cm^2
=	1 × 10^8	cgs emu of magnetic flux density

weber per square metre (Wb / m^2)
Unit of magnetic flux density

=	1	T (tesla)
=	10 000	cgs units of induction
=	10 000	cgs emu of induction
=	3.336 × 10^{-7}	cgs esu of induction
=	2.654 × 10^{-8}	cgs esu of magnetization
=	10 000	Gs (gauss)
=	1 × 10^8	lines / m^2
=	1 × 10^8	Mx / m^2

week, mean calendar (wk)
Unit of time

= 7	d	(mean solar)		
= 168	h	"	"	
= 10 080	min	"	"	
= 0.230 137	mo	(mean calendar)		
= 0.019 178 082	yr	(calendar)		
= 0.019 164 622	yr	(sideral)		
= 0.019 165 365	tr	(tropical)		

wey (UK)
Unit of volume or capacity

= 40	bushels	(UK)
= 51.374	ft^3	
= 1454.7	dm^3 or L	
= 1	load	(UK)

wey (UK)
Unit of mass

= 114.306	kg	
= 252	lb	
= 1	load	(UK)

– Y –

yard (yd)
Unit of length

= 914.4	mm
= 91.44	cm
= 0.9144	m
= 0.5	fathom
= 9.14×10^{-4}	km
= $5.681\ 81 \times 10^{-4}$	mi (statute)
= $4.937\ 36 \times 10^{-4}$	mi (nautical)

year, calendar (yr)
Unit of time

= 365	d	(mean solar)
= 8760	h	" "
= 525 600	min	" "
= 31 536 000	s	" "
= 12	mo	(mean calendar)
= 52.142 857	wk	" "
= 0.999 298 14	yr	(sideral)
= 0.999 336 90	yr	(tropical)

year, leap (yr)
Unit of time

= 366	d	(mean solar)
= 8784	h	" "

year, sideral (yr)
Unit of time

= 365.256 36	d	(mean solar)
= 8766.1526	h	" "
= 31 558 150	s	" "

year, tropical (yr)
Unit of time

= 365.242 19	d	(mean solar)
= 8765.8126	h	" "
= 31 556 926	s	" "

SI UNITS

The name Système International d'Unités (International System of Units), with the international abbreviation SI, was adopted by the 11th Conférence Générale des Poids et Mesures in 1960.

This system includes three classes of units:

- base units
- supplementary units
- derived units

which together form the coherent system of SI units.

Base units

The International System of Units is founded on the seven base units listed in table 1.

Table 1

Quantity	Name of base SI unit	Symbol
length	metre	m
mass	kilogram[1]	kg
time	second	s
electric current	ampere	A
thermodynamic temperature	kelvin[2]	K
amount of substance	mole[3]	mol
luminous intensity	candela	cd

Note 1: The kilogram is the only base unit that contains a prefix. The mass of a given object is a constant characteristic of that object and represents the resistance to change of motion.

The weight of an object is not a constant, since it results from
a) the mass of the object, and
b) the gravitation pull of the earth.

The unit of mass is the kilogram. Since weight represents the gravitational pull of the earth, it is a force, and the unit of weight is therefore the newton.

Note 2: While the base unit of temperature is the kelvin, for non scientific purposes temperature is expressed in degrees Celsius (°C). A temperature change of 1 K = 1°C. The word degree (or its symbol) is not used with kelvin (K). Celsius corresponds to the previously named Centigrade scale whose name was changed to Celsius in 1948 to avoid confusion in countries where a "grade" is a plane angle and a centigrade is 1 / 100 of that angle. (See temperature table)

Note 3: The mole is associated with atoms or molecules and will not be normally encountered. 1 mole equals that amount of substance containing 6.022×10^{23} atoms or molecules. This is the number of atoms in 0.012 kg of carbon 12. (Therefore 1 kg of carbon 12 contains 5.02×10^{25} atoms)

Supplementary units

The Conférence Générale des Poids et Mesures has not classified certain units of the International System under either base units or derived units.

These units, listed in table 2, are called "supplementary units" and may be regarded either as base units or as derived units.

Table 2

Quantity	Name of supplementary SI unit	Symbol
plane angle	radian	rad
solid angle	steradian	sr

However, in October 1980 the International Committee of Weights and Measures decided to interpret the class of supplementary units in the International System as a class of dimensionless derived units for which the General Conference of Weights and Measures leaves open the possibility of using these or not in expressions of derived units of the International System.

The 360° circle of angular measure, inherited from the Babylonians, is likely to be around for a long time. If angular measure is changed, it will be necessary to alter all lines of latitude and longitude, and also revise the time zones around the earth.

Angles will, in common usage, be measured in degrees as in the past. The "decimal degree" is now preferred over the use of degrees, minutes, and seconds. For example, the use of 61.50° is preferred over the use of 61°30′, except possibly for maps.

To handle problems in curvilinear motion, rotation, rolling and so on, SI needs a measure of angle. The sexagesimal degree (one revolution = 360°) is internationally known and appears as a customary unit, but is not taken as fundamental. This is partly due to the existence of an alternative centesimal system [1 ...^{r} (revolution) = 400 ...^{g} (grades); 1 ...^{g} (grade) = 100 ...^{cg} (centigrades)].

SI takes the radian (rad) as the angle subtended at the center of a circle by an arc equal in length to the radius. The unit is thus a numerical ratio, metres per metre. Since one complete turn takes a point on the circumference completely round a distance $2\pi \times$ radius, 2π rad = one complete turn.

It is worth noting that for the calculations required by astronavigation the units at present in use, the degree, the nautical mile and the knot, will not be replaceable by SI units. This is because there is a simple arithmetical relationship between time and the earth's angular velocity (it rotates 15° in 1 h) and between angle and distance on the earth's surface 1° difference of latitude along a meridian = 60 n mile (nautical miles).

A measure often used in theory is that of solid angle. SI specifies, again as a supplementary unit, the steradian (sr). This is the solid angle subtended at the centre of a sphere by any portion of its surface equal in area to the square of the radius, and is thus the three dimensional equivalent of the radian. Since the surface area of a sphere is given by $4\pi\ r^2$ it follows that 4π sr = one complete sphere.

Supplementary units (cont'd)
Note that, although a cone has a solid angle at its vertex, this is not the same as the 'angle of the cone', which is double the plane angle between a generator and the axis. A solid angle can be subtended by any irregular shape; it is only the area intercepted on the sphere that determines the value.

Definitions of base units
metre (m)
the metre is the length of the path travelled by light in vacuum during a time interval of 1 / 299 792 458 of a second. (17th CGPM, 1983).

kilogram (kg)
The kilogram is the unit of mass (not force); it is equal to the mass of the international prototype of the kilogram. (3rd CGPM, 1901).

second (s)
The second is the duration of 9 192 631 770 periods of the radiation corresponding to the transition between the two hyperfine levels of the ground state of the cesium − 133 atom. (13th CGPM, 1967).

ampere (A)
The ampere is that constant current which, if maintained in two straight parallel conductors of infinite length, of negligible circular cross section, and placed 1 metre apart in vacuum, would produce between these conductors a force equal to 2×10^{-7} newton per metre of length. (9th CGPM, 1948).

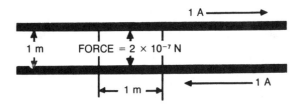

The unit is named after André Marie Ampère, French (1775–1836).

kelvin (K)
The kelvin, unit of thermodynamic temperature, is the fraction 1 / 273,16 of the thermodynamic temperature of the triple point of water. (13th CGPM, 1967). In addition to the thermodynamic temperature, Celsius temperature (formerly called Centigrade) is widely used. The triple point of water is the equilibrium temperature (0.01°C or 273,16 K) between pure ice, air-free water and water vapour.

The standard temperature of the triple point of water is provided by a special cell, an evacuated glass cylinder containing pure water. When the cell is cooled until a mantle of ice forms around the reentrant well, the temperature at the interface of solid, liquid, and vapor is 273,16 K (0,01 °C). Thermometers to be calibrated are placed in the reentrant well.

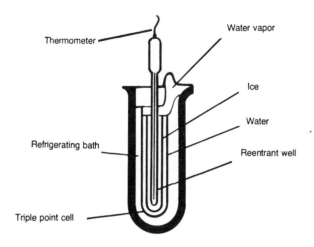

The kelvin scale (sometimes called the absolute scale) is very useful in science, for instance, in the study of gas laws. There are no negative readings on the kelvin scale since the lowest temperature, $-273.15°C$ is called zero kelvin or absolute zero.

The kelvin scale is named after Lord Kelvin, a British scientist (1824–1907). His scale is nothing more than the Celsius scale as far as ratio is concerned.

mole (mol)
The mole is the amount of substance of a system that contains as many elementary entities as there are atoms in 0.012 kilogram of carbon – 12. (14th CGPM, 1971).

candela (cd)
The candela is the luminous intensity, in a given direction, of a source that emits monochromatic radiation of frequency 540×10^{-12} hertz and that has a radian intensity in that direction of 1 / 683 watt per steradian. (16th CGPM, 1979).

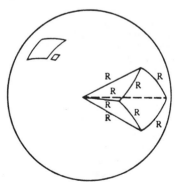

One candela will produce a luminous flux of 1 lumen within a solid angle of 1 steradian.

Definitions of supplementary units

radian (rad)

The radian is the plane angle between two radii of a circle that cut off, on the circumference, an arc equal in length to the radius.

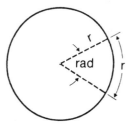

When the length of the arc of a circle is equal to its radius, the subtended angle is equal to one radian. One radian is very nearly equal to 57.3 degrees.

steradian (sr)

The steradian is the solid angle that, having its vertex in the center of a sphere, cuts off an area of the surface of the sphere equal to that of a square with sides of length equal to the radius of the sphere.

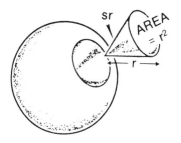

Derived units

Derived units are expressed algebraically in terms of base units and / or supplementary units. Their symbols are obtained by means of the mathematical signs of multiplication and division; for example, the SI unit for velocity is metre per second (m / s) and the SI unit for angular velocity is radian per second (rad / s).

For some of the derived SI units, special names and symbols exist; those approved by the Conférence Générale des Poids et Mesures are listed in tables 3 and 4.

It may sometimes be advantageous to express derived units in terms of other derived units having special names; for example, the SI unit for electric dipole moment is usually expressed as C·m instead of A·s·m.

Table 3

Quantity	Special name of derived SI unit	Symbol	Expressed in terms of base or supplementary SI units or in terms of other derived SI units
frequency	hertz	Hz	$1 \text{ Hz} = 1 \text{ s}^{-1}$
force	newton	N	$1 \text{ N} = 1 \text{ kg·m/s}^2$
pressure, stress	pascal	Pa	$1 \text{ Pa} = 1 \text{ N/m}^2$
energy, work, quantity of heat	joule	J	$1 \text{ J} = 1 \text{ N·m}$
power	watt	W	$1 \text{ W} = 1 \text{ J/s}$
electric charge, quantity of electricity	coulomb	C	$1 \text{ C} = 1 \text{ A·s}$
electric potential, potential difference, tension, electro-motive force	volt	V	$1 \text{V} = 1 \text{ J/C}$
electric capacitance	farad	F	$1 \text{ F} = 1 \text{ C/V}$
electric resistance	ohm	Ω	$1\Omega = 1 \text{ V/A}$
electric, conductance	siemens	S	$1 \text{ S} = 1\Omega^{-1}$
flux of magnetic induction, magnetic flux	weber	Wb	$1 \text{ Wb} = 1 \text{ V·s}$
magnetic flux density, magnetic induction	tesla	T	$1 \text{ T} = 1 \text{ Wb/m}^2$
inductance	henry	H	$1 \text{ H} = 1 \text{ Wb/A}$
Celsius temperature	degree Celsius	°C	$1 \text{ °C} = 1 \text{ K}$
luminous flux	lumen	lm	$1 \text{ lm} = 1 \text{ cd·sr}$
illuminance	lux	lx	$1 \text{ lx} = 1 \text{ lm/m}^2$

Table 4
Derived SI units with special names accepted
for the sake of safeguarding human health. (ISO 1000)

Quantity	Special name of derived SI unit	Symbol	Expressed in terms of base units or derived SI units
activity (of a radionuclide)	becquerel	Bq	$1\ Bq = 1\ s^{-1}$
absorbed dose, specific energy imparted, kerma, absorbed dose index	gray	Gy	$1\ Gy = 1\ J / kg$
dose equivalent	sievert	Sv	$1\ Sv = 1\ J / kg$

Definitions of derived units with special names

becquerel (Bq)
The becquerel is the activity of a radionuclide having one spontaneous nuclear transition per second. The unit is named after Antoine Henri Becquerel, French, (1852–1908).

coulomb (C)
The coulomb is the quantity of electricity transported in 1 second by a current of 1 ampere. The unit is named after Charles Auguste de Coulomb, French, (1736–1806).

degree Celsius (°C)
The degree Celsius is equal to the kelvin and is used in place of the kelvin for expressing Celsius temperature (symbol t) defined by the equation $t = T - T_0$ where T is the symbol of the thermodynamic temperature and $T_0 = 275.16\ K$ by definition. (The unit is named after Anders Celsius, Swedish, (1701–1744).

farad (F)
The farad is the capacitance of a capacitor between the equipotential surfaces of which there appears a difference of potential of 1 volt when the capacitor is charged by a quantity of electricity equal to 1 coulomb. The unit is named after Michael Faraday, English, (1791–1867).

gray (Gy)
The gray is the energy imparted by ionizing radiation to a mass of matter corresponding to 1 joule per kilogram. The unit is named after Louis Harold Gray, English, (1905–   ).

henry (H)
The henry is the inductance of a closed circuit in which an electromotive force of 1 volt is produced when the electric current varies uniformly at a rate of 1 ampere per second. The unit is named after Joseph Henry, American, (1799–1878).

hertz (Hz)
The hertz is the frequency of a periodic phenomenon of which the periodic time is 1 second. The unit is named after Henry R. Hertz, German, (1857–1894).

joule (J)
The joule is the work done when the point of application of a force of 1 newton is displaced a distance of 1 metre in the direction of the force. The unit is named after James Prescott Joule, English, (1818–1889).

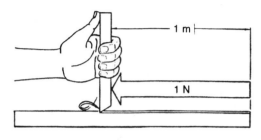

1 joule = 1 newton × 1 metre

lumen (lm)
The lumen is the luminous flux emitted in a solid angle of 1 steradian by a point source having an intensity of 1 candela. This latin name means light. The point source is at the vertex of the solid angle.

lux (lx)
The lux is the illuminance produced by a flux of 1 lumen uniformly distributed over 1 square metre. This latin name also means light.

newton (N)
The newton is the force that, when applied to a body having a mass of 1 kilogram, gives the body an acceleration of 1 metre per second squared. The unit is named after Sir Isaac Newton, English, (1642-1727).

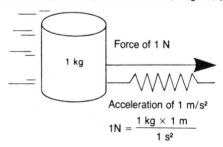

Force of 1 N

Acceleration of 1 m/s²

$$1N = \frac{1 \text{ kg} \times 1 \text{ m}}{1 \text{ s}^2}$$

For example, the force required to give a mass of 10 kg an acceleration of 8 m / s² is 80 newtons (N).

ohm (Ω)

The ohm is the electric resistance between two points of a conductor when a constant difference of potential of 1 volt, applied between these two points, produces in the conductor a current of 1 ampere, this conductor not being the source of any electromotive force. The unit is named after George S. Ohm, German, (1787–1854).

pascal (Pa)

The pascal is the pressure (or stress) which is produced when a force of 1 newton is applied to an area of 1 square metre. The unit is named after Blaise Pascal, French, (1623–1662).

It has been suggested that an apple tossed into the air strikes the hand, on falling, with a force of about one newton. An average size apple about 100 grams is attracted to the earth by gravity with a force of about 1 newton (N). If the same apple is made into apple sauce and spread over an area of one square metre, the pressure exerted would be equal to 1 pascal (Pa).

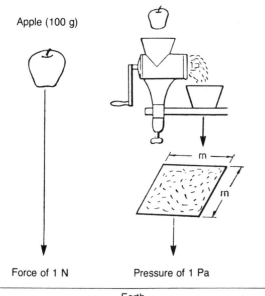

Apple (100 g)

Force of 1 N   Pressure of 1 Pa

Earth

Visual comparison of one newton and one pascal.

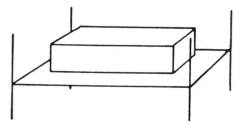

This block has a mass of 50 kilograms. Therefore it exerts a downward force of 490 newtons (50 kg × 9,81 m / s²). The block acts on an area of 2 square metres.

$$\frac{490 \text{ N}}{2 \text{ m}^2} = 245 \text{ N} / \text{m}^2 = 245 \text{ Pa}$$

Note: Although the newton is defined in terms of a mass and an acceleration, it also applies to stationary objects, and to every application where a force is involved.

$$
\begin{aligned}
\text{Force} &= \text{mass} \times \text{acceleration} \\
&= 1 \text{ kg} \times 9.81 \text{ m} / \text{s}^2 \\
&= 9.81 \text{ N}
\end{aligned}
$$

Whenever a force is applied in opposition to gravity, g must be considered.

[g (acceleration due to gravity) = 9.81 m / s²]

In the above example, we express the force as 490 newtons, not 50 kilograms. 9.81 N is also the force needed to keep the mass of 1 kg suspended in space.

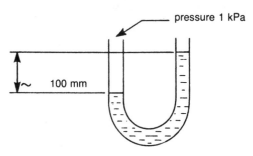

One kilopascal (kPa) is equal to approximately the pressure exerted by a 100-mm column of water at 15.5°C

siemens (S)
The siemens is the electrical conductance between two points of a conductor when a constant current of 1 ampere in the conductor produces a difference of potential of 1 volt between these two points and when the conductor itself is not the seat of any electromotive force. The unit is named after Werner Von Siemens, German, (1816–1892).

sievert (Sv)
The sievert is the dose equivalent when the absorbed dose of ionizing radiation is one joule per kilogram.

tesla (T)
The tesla is the magnetic induction that is equal to 1 weber per square metre. The unit is named after Nicola Tesla, Croatian, (1856–1943).

volt (V)
The volt is the electric potential difference between two points of a conductor that is carrying a constant current of 1 ampere, when the power dissipated between these two points is equal to 1 watt. The unit is named after Count Alessandro Volta, Italian, (1745–1827).

watt (W)
The watt is the power that produces energy at the rate of 1 joule per second. The unit is named after James Watt, Scot, (1736–1819).

weber (Wb)
The weber is the magnetic flux that, when linking a circuit of one turn, produces in that circuit an electromotive force of 1 volt as the flux is reduced to zero at a uniform rate in 1 second. The unit is named after Weilhelm E. Weber, German, (1804–1891).

Table 5
Some common derived units of SI

Quantity	Name	Symbol
acceleration	metre per second squared	m / s^2
angular acceleration	radian per second squared	rad / s^2
angular velocity	radian per second	rad / s
area	square metre	m^2
concentration	mole per cubic metre	mol / m^3
current density	ampere per square metre	A / m^2
density, mass	kilogram per cubic metre	kg / m^3
electric charge density	coulomb per cubic metre	C / m^3
electric field strength	volt per metre	V / m
electric flux density	coulomb per square metre	C / m^2
energy density	joule per cubic metre	J / m^3
entropy	joule per kelvin	J / K
heat capacity	joule per kelvin	J / K
heat flux density	watt per square metre	W / m^2
luminance	candela per square metre	cd / m^2
magnetic field strength	ampere per metre	A / m
molar energy	joule per mole	J / mol
molar entropy	joule per mole kelvin	$J / (mol \cdot K)$
molar heat capacity	joule per mole kelvin	$J / (mol \cdot K)$
moment of force	newton metre	$N \cdot m$
permeability	henry per metre	H / m
permittivity	farad per metre	F / m
radiance	watt per sq. metre steradian	$W / (m^2 \cdot sr)$
radiant intensity	watt per steradian	W / sr
specific heat capacity	joule per kilogram kelvin	$J / (kg \cdot K)$
specific energy	joule per kilogram	J / kg
specific entropy	joule per kilogram kelvin	$J / (kg \cdot K)$
specific volume	cubic metre per kilogram	m^3 / kg
surface tension	newton per metre	N / m
thermal conductivity	watt per metre kelvin	$W / (m \cdot K)$
velocity	metre per second	m / s
viscosity, dynamic	pascal second	$Pa \cdot s$
viscosity, kinematic	square metre per second	m^2 / s
volume	cubic metre	m^3
wave number	one per metre	m^{-1}

Derived units are formed from the products or quotients of other units. Multiplication of two or more units is indicated by a dot (·) centred between the unit symbols, e.g. N·m. Division of one unit by another is indicated by a solidus (/) e.g. 50 kg / m^2, by the use of negative exponent, e.g. 50 kg·m^{-2}, or simply by $\dfrac{50 \text{ kg}}{m^2}$

There are certain units outside the SI which are recognized by the Comité International des Poids et Mesures (CIPM) as having to be retained because of their practical importance (table 6) or for use in specialized fields (table 7).

Table 6

Quantity	Name of unit	Unit symbol	Definition
time	minute	min	1 min = 60 s
	hour	h	1 h = 60 min
	day	d	1 d = 24 h
plane[1]	degree	°	1...° = $(\pi / 180)$ rad
angle	minute	'	1...' = $(1 / 60)$°
	second	"	1..." = $(1 / 60)$'
capacity[2] (or volume)	litre	L	1 L = 1 dm^3
mass	tonne	t	1 t = 1000 kg
marine and aerial distance	nautical mile	n mi	1 n mi = 1852 m
marine and aerial velocity	knot	kn	1 kn = 1 n mi / h = $(1852 / 3600)$ m / s = 0.5144 m / s
land area	hectare	ha	1 ha = 10 000 m^2
pressure	standard atmosphere	atm	1 atm = 101.325 kPa
temperature[3]	degree Celsius	°C	An interval of 1°C = 1 K By definition 1°C $\hat{=}$ 273.15 K

Note: this sign ($\hat{=}$) means: corresponds to

1) Decimal subdivisions of plane angle degree may be used in place of minutes and seconds.

2) It is worth noting the subtle difference between volume and capacity. A cubic container measuring 1 m × 1 m × 1 m has a volume of one cubic metre (1 m^3), but a capacity to hold 1000 L of a liquid, or one kilolitre.

3) Celsius is the only name with a capital letter. The symbol (°) is not used with kelvin. Not 1 degree kelvin (°K), but 1 kelvin (K).

Dates and time
1990 09 28 or 1990-09-28 – typing, printing, and handwriting.
19900928 – computer or data transmission.

Time is expressed in the hour-minute-second sequence using the 24-hour clock. 16:30 and not 4.30 p.m. – 03:25 and not 3:25 a.m.

11:59:59 means one second (1 s) before noon.
23:59:59 means one second (1 s) before midnight.
00:00:01 means one second (1 s) after noon or midnight .

Table 7

Quantity	Name of unit	Unit symbol	Definition
energy	electronvolt	eV	1 electronvolt is the kinetic energy acquired by an electron in passing through a potential difference of 1 volt in vacuum; 1 eV = 1.602 19 × 10^{-19} J (approximately).
mass of an atom	atomic mass unit	u	1 (unified) atomic mass unit is equal to the fraction 1/12 of the mass of an atom of the nuclide ^{12}C; 1 u = 1.660 53 × 10^{-27} kg (approximately).
length	astronomic unit	AU[1]	1 AU = 1.495 979 × 10^{11} m
	parsec	pc	1 parsec is the distance of which 1 astronomic unit subtends an angle of 1 second of arc; 1 pc = 206 265 AU = 3.085 678 × 10^{16} m (approximately).
	light year	l·y·	1 l·y· = 9.460 55 × 10^{15} m
pressure of fluid	bar[2]	bar	1 bar = 10^5 Pa

1) The unit has no international symbol; AU is the abbreviation of the English name; UA is the abbreviation of the French name; AE is the abbreviation of the German name, etc.

2) The bar is not mentioned by CIPM in this group of units; in many countries, however, there are special requirements for this unit.

Table 8

Metric units that should not be used with the SI

Quantity	Name of unit	Unit symbol	Definition
length	micron	μ	$1\ \mu$ = $1\ \mu m$
	fermi	fm	1 fermi = 1 fm = $(10^{-15}\ m)$
volume	stère	st	1 st = $1\ m^3$
	lambda	λ	$1\ \lambda$ = $1\ \mu L$ = $1\ mm^3$
mass	metric carat	–	1 carat = 200 mg
	gamma	γ	$1\ \gamma$ = $1\ \mu g$
force	kilogram-force (kilopond)	kgf	1 kgf = 9.806 65 N
	dyne	dyn	1 dyn = $10\ \mu N$
pressure	torr	–	1 torr = 1 mmHg
			= (101.325 / 760) Pa
energy	calorie	cal	1 cal = 4.1868 J
	erg	erg	1 erg = $0.1\ \mu J$
viscosity (dynamic)	poise	P	1 P = $1\ dyn \cdot s\ /\ cm^2$
			= 0.1 Pa·s
viscosity (kinematic)	stokes	St	1 St = $1\ cm^2\ /\ s$
magnetic induction	gamma	γ	$1\ \gamma$ $\hat{=}$ 0.1 nT
magnetic field strength	oersted	Oe	1 Oe $\hat{=}$ $(1000\ /\ 4\pi)$ A / m
magnetic flux	maxwell	Mx	1 Mx $\hat{=}$ $0.01\ \mu Wb$
magnetic flux density	gauss	Gs	1 Gs $\hat{=}$ 0.1 mT
illuminance	phot	ph	1 ph = 10 klx
luminance	stilb	sb	1 sb = $1\ cd\ /\ cm^2$
X rays	X unit	–	(see note)

Note: This special unit was employed to express wavelengths of X rays; 1 × unit = 1.002×10^{-4} nm (approximately).

This sign ($\hat{=}$) means: corresponds to.

Conversion of metric units of area
(Square measures)

Unit	Symbol		Multiples and Sub-Multiples		
square kilometre	km^2	=	$1\,000\,000\ m^2$	=	$10^6\ m^2$
square hectometre	hm^2	=	$10\,000\ m^2$	=	$10^4\ m^2$
square decametre	dam^2	=	$100\ m^2$	=	$10^2\ m^2$
square metre	m^2	=	$1\ m^2$	=	$10^0\ m^2$
square decimetre	dm^2	=	$0,01\ m^2$	=	$10^{-2}\ m^2$
square centimetre	cm^2	=	$0,000\,1\ m^2$	=	$10^{-4}\ m^2$
square millimetre	mm^2	=	$0,000\,001\ m^2$	=	$10^{-6}\ m^2$

km^2	hm^2	dam^2	m^2	dm^2	cm^2	mm^2
1	10^2	10^4	10^6	10^8	10^{10}	10^{12}
	1	10^2	10^4	10^6	10^8	10^{10}
		1	10^2	10^4	10^6	10^8
			1	10^2	10^4	10^6
				1	10^2	10^4
					1	10^2

mm^2	cm^2	dm^2	m^2	dam^2	hm^2	km^2
1	10^{-2}	10^{-4}	10^{-6}	10^{-8}	10^{-10}	10^{-12}
	1	10^{-2}	10^{-4}	10^{-6}	10^{-8}	10^{-10}
		1	10^{-2}	10^{-4}	10^{-6}	10^{-8}
			1	10^{-2}	10^{-4}	10^{-6}
				1	10^{-2}	10^{-4}
					1	10^{-2}

Note: hm^2 (square hectometre) $\hat{=}$ ha (hectare)
dam^2 (square decametre) $\hat{=}$ a (are)

Terminology: An area of 4 cm^2 is one with sides 2 cm in length.
(read as four square centimetres)
A 4 – cm square is one with sides 4 cm in length
and has an area of 16 cm^2.

Area calculations in SI units
Example 1
A road 1 km long and 8 m wide is to be covered with asphalt. The asphalt needed is 14 L / m^2 and the density of the asphalt is 1,5 kg / L. Express in kilograms (kg) and tonnes (t) the total mass (wt) of asphalt required?

$1\,000\ m \times 8\ m = 8\,000\ m^2$
$8\,000\ m^2 \times 14\ L/m^2 = 112\,000\ L$
$112\,000\ L \times 1,5\ kg/L = 168\,000\ kg$
$= 168\ t$

Example 2
How much area in square metres would 1 cm^3 of oil cover on water if the oil film were 4 nm (nanometres) in thickness?

$1\ cm^3 = 1\ cm^2 \times 1\ cm$
area of oil = volume of oil / film thickness
$1\ cm = 10^7\ nm$ or $1\ nm = 10^{-7}\ cm$
$1\ cm^3 \div 4 \times 10^{-7}\ cm = 0,25 \times 10^7\ cm^2$
$0,25 \times 10^7\ cm^2 \div 1 \times 10^4\ cm^2/m^2 = 2,5 \times 10^2\ m^2$
$= 250\ m^2$

Example 3

What is the average thickness in nanometres (nm) of 0,1 mm^3 of stearic acid, covering a total area of 400 cm^2 of water?

1 mm^3 = 0,001 cm^3

then 0,1 mm^3 = 1×10^{-4} cm^3

film thickness in cm = volume / area

1×10^{-4} cm^3 ÷ 4×10^2 cm^2 = $0{,}25 \times 10^{-6}$ cm

$\qquad\qquad\qquad\qquad\qquad\qquad\quad$ = $2{,}5 \times 10^{-7}$ cm

$\qquad\qquad\qquad\qquad\qquad\qquad\quad$ = $2{,}5 \times 10^{-6}$ mm

$\qquad\qquad\qquad\qquad\qquad\qquad\quad$ = 2,5 nm

Conversion of metric units of length

(Linear measures)

Unit	Symbol	Multiples and Sub-Multiples			
megametre	Mm	=	1 000 000 m	=	10^6 m
kilometre	km	=	1 000 m	=	10^3 m
metre	m	=	1 m	=	10^0 m
millimetre	mm	=	0,001 m	=	10^{-3} m
micrometre	μm	=	0,000 001 m	=	10^{-6} m

km	hm	dam	m	dm	cm	mm	μm
1	10^1	10^2	10^3	10^4	10^5	10^6	10^9
	1	10^1	10^2	10^3	10^4	10^5	10^8
		1	10^1	10^2	10^3	10^4	10^7
			1	10^1	10^2	10^3	10^6
				1	10^1	10^2	10^5
					1	10^1	10^4
						1	10^3

μm	mm	cm	dm	m	dam	hm	km
1	10^{-3}	10^{-4}	10^{-5}	10^{-6}	10^{-7}	10^{-8}	10^{-9}
	1	10^{-3}	10^{-4}	10^{-5}	10^{-6}	10^{-7}	10^{-8}
		1	10^{-3}	10^{-4}	10^{-5}	10^{-6}	10^{-7}
			1	10^{-3}	10^{-4}	10^{-5}	10^{-6}
				1	10^{-3}	10^{-4}	10^{-5}
					1	10^{-3}	10^{-4}
						1	10^{-3}

Length and time

Here are some examples of typical measures in length and time using permissible SI units, illustrating variations that may be found in practice.

One light year (l·y·)	=	9.46×10^{15} m
Distance to the moon	=	384 000 km
Radius of earth	=	6378 km
Height (average) of a man	=	1750 mm
Thickness of cigarette paper	=	25 μm
Effective diameter of water molecule	=	4.10×10^{-10} m
Half life of radium (from uranium)	=	1590 years
Half life of polonium (from thorium)	=	3×10^{-7} second

Where magnitudes differ considerably it is better to use metres only for computation.

Example:
Compare the thickness of a cigarette paper with the diameter of a molecule of water.

Our table gives one in μm (micrometre), the other in m (metre).
Then, thickness of paper = 2.5×10^{-5} m
     diameter of molecule = 4.1×10^{-10} m
     hence ratio 2.5 / 4.1 $\times 10^5 = 6.1 \times 10^4 = 61\ 000$

The effective diameter of a water molecule is less than 1 / 60 000 part of the thickness of a cigarette paper.

Length calculations in SI units
Example
A standard plywood wallboard is 1200 mm by 3000 mm long. Is this sufficient to close an opening 60 cm wide by 6 m long?

1200 mm $\times$ 3000 mm = 3 600 000 mm^2
60 cm = 600 mm
6 m = 600 cm = 6000 mm
600 mm $\times$ 6000 mm = 3 600 000 mm^2
Yes. (Two identical pieces cut lengthwise).

Conversion of metric units of mass

Unit	Symbol	Multiples and Sub-Multiples		
megagram	Mg	=	1 000 000 g	= 10^6 g
kilogram	kg	=	1 000 g	= 10^3 g
gram	g	=	1 g	= 10^0 g
decigram	dg	=	0.1 g	= 10^{-1} g
centigram	cg	=	0.01 g	= 10^{-2} g
milligram	mg	=	0.001 g	= 10^{-3} g
microgram	μg	=	0.000 001 g	= 10^{-6} g

Mg	kg	g	dg	cg	mg	μg
1	10^3	10^6	10^7	10^8	10^9	10^{12}
	1	10^3	10^4	10^5	10^6	10^9
		1	10^1	10^2	10^3	10^6
			1	10^1	10^2	10^5
				1	10^1	10^4
					1	10^3

μg	mg	cg	dg	g	kg	Mg
1	10^{-3}	10^{-4}	10^{-5}	10^{-6}	10^{-9}	10^{-12}
	1	10^{-1}	10^{-2}	10^{-3}	10^{-6}	10^{-9}
		1	10^{-1}	10^{-2}	10^{-5}	10^{-8}
			1	10^{-1}	10^{-4}	10^{-7}
				1	10^{-3}	10^{-6}
					1	10^{-3}

The kilogram is the only unit whose name, for historical reasons, contains a prefix. Names of decimal multiples and sub-multiples of the unit of mass are formed by attaching prefixes to the word gram. 1 000 kg must be adjusted to:

$$10^3 \times 10^3 \text{ g} = 1 \text{ Mg (megagram)}$$
$$= 1 \text{ t (tonne)}$$
Do not use kkg to express 1 000 kg

Considerable confusion exists in the use of the term **weight** to mean either **force** or **mass**. Weight is mass under the influence of gravity, and is a force. In space, away from any gravitational influence, the weight of an object will be zero, but its mass will remain the same as on earth. The downward force exerted by a mass of one kilogram on a surface at sea level on earth is expressed as:

$$F = 1 \text{ kg} \times 9.81 \text{ m / s}^2$$
$$= 9.81 \text{ N}$$

The same mass standing on the surface of the moon, where the gravitational acceleration is 1.62 m / s^2 would weigh 1.62 N or approximately 6 times less.

Mass calculations in SI units
Example 1
One gram of gel covers approximately 5×10^6 cm^2 of surface. Express this as micrograms of gel per square metre.

$$\frac{5 \times 10^6 \text{ cm}^2}{1 \times 10^4 \text{ cm}^2 / \text{m}^2} = 5 \times 10^2 \text{ m}^2$$

$$1 \text{ g} = 1 \times 10^6 \text{ }\mu\text{g}$$

$$\frac{1 \times 10^6 \text{ }\mu\text{g}}{5 \times 10^2 \text{ m}^2} = \frac{10 \times 10^5 \text{ }\mu\text{g}}{5 \times 10^2 \text{ m}^2}$$

$$= 2 \times 10^3 \text{ }\mu\text{g / m}^2$$

Example 2
A wall 9 m long and 2.8 m high is to be plastered to an average thickness of 10 mm. The density of the plaster to be used is 2 500 kg / m^3. What is the mass of plaster involved?

$$9 \text{ m} \times 2.8 \text{ m} = 25.2 \text{ m}^2$$
$$25.2 \text{ m}^2 \times 0.01 \text{ m} = 0.252 \text{ m}^3$$
$$0.252 \text{ m}^3 \times 2 \text{ 500 kg / m}^3 = 630 \text{ kg}$$

Example 3
A copper pipe 6 m long has an outside diameter of 10 mm and a wall thickness of 2 mm. The density of copper is 8.9 Mg / m^3. What is the mass of the pipe?

$$\text{Volume of pipe} = 0.785 \text{ 4} \times (D^2 - d^2) \times l$$
$$= 0.785 \text{ 4} \times 36 \text{ mm}^2 \times 6 \text{ 000 mm}$$
$$= 169 \text{ 646 mm}^3$$
$$8.9 \text{ Mg / m}^3 = 8.9 \text{ Mg / } 10^9 \text{ mm}^3$$
$$= 8.9 \text{ kg / } 10^6 \text{ mm}^3$$
$$= 8.9 \text{ g / } 10^3 \text{ mm}^3$$

$$\frac{8.9 \text{ g} \times 169 \text{ 646 mm}^3}{1 \text{ 000 mm}^3} = 1 \text{ 510 g}$$

Conversion of metric units of volume
(Cubic measures)

Unit	Symbol	Multiples and Sub-Multiples		
cubic kilometre	km³	= 1 000 000 000 m³	=	10^9 m³
cubic hectometre	hm³	= 1 000 000 m³	=	10^6 m³
cubic decametre	dam³	= 1 000 m³	=	10^3 m³
cubic metre	m³	= 1 m³	=	10^0 m³
cubic decimetre	dm³	= 0,001 m³	=	10^{-3} m³
cubic centimetre	cm³	= 0,000 001 m³	=	10^{-6} m³
cubic millimetre	mm³	= 0,000 000 001 m³	=	10^{-9} m³

m³	dm³	cm³	mm³
1	10^3	10^6	10^9
	1	10^3	10^6
		1	10^3

mm³	cm³	dm³	m³
1	10^{-3}	10^{-6}	10^{-9}
	1	10^{-3}	10^{-6}
		1	10^{-3}

In the Metric system, cubic measure units are directly related to the units of measure for capacity. Volume applies to solids; capacity applies to fluids and gases. This simplifies design of storage facilities, etc., in that a tank requiring a capacity of 1000 litres will have a volume of 1000 cubic decimetres (dm³) or 1 cubic metre (m³).

$$1 \text{ cubic centimetre (cm}^3) = 1 \text{ millilitre (mL)}$$
$$1 \text{ cubic decimetre (dm}^3) = 1 \text{ litre (L)}$$
$$1 \text{ cubic metre (m}^3) \quad = 1 \text{ kilolitre (kL)}$$

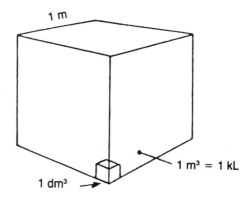

One cubic metre

litre (L)

The litre was originally defined as the volume occupied by the mass of 1 kg of water at 3,98°C. Careful determinations subsequently established its volume as being 1,000 028 dm^3 and the litre was then declared a special name for the cubic decimetre, and its use limited to the measurement of liquids and gases. The use of the name litre for high-precision measurements might conflict with the old value and is not advisable.

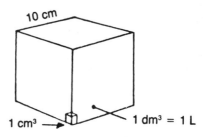

One cubic decimetre

Volume calculations in SI units
Example 1
Calculate the total volume of water which falls on a field of area 2.37 hectares during a day when the rainfall is 19 mm.

2.37 ha × 10 000 m^2 / ha = 23 700 m^2

23 700 m^2 × 0.019 m (19 mm) = 450.3 m^3 or 450 kL.

Example 2
A cube has a volume of 1.137 × 10^3 cm^3. What is this volume in cubic metres, cubic millimetres, and litres?

$$\text{Cubic metres} = \frac{1.137 \times 10^3 \ cm^3}{1 \times 10^6 \ cm^3 / m^3} = 1.137 \times 10^{-3} \ m^3$$

$$\text{Cubic millimetres} = \frac{1.137 \times 10^3 \ cm^3}{1 \times 10^{-3} \ cm^3 / mm^3} = 1.137 \times 10^6 \ mm^3$$

$$\text{Litres} = \frac{1.137 \times 10^3 \ cm^3}{1 \times 10^3 \ cm^3 / L} = 1.137 \ L$$

Example 3
A container is 50 mm in diameter and 110 mm high. What is its volume in cubic millimetres, cubic metres, and litres?

$$\text{Cubic millimetres} = (50 \ mm)^2 \times 0.785 \ 4 \times 110 \ mm$$
$$= 215 \ 985 \ mm^3$$
$$\text{rounded to} = 216 \ 000 \ mm^3$$

$$\text{Cubic metres} = \frac{216 \times 10^3 \ mm^3}{1 \times 10^9 \ mm^3 / m^3} = 216 \times 10^{-6} \ m^3$$

$$\text{Litres} = \frac{216 \times 10^3 \ mm^3}{1 \times 10^6 \ mm^3 / L} = 216 \times 10^{-3} \ L$$

Conversion of metric units of capacity
(Cubic measures)

Unit	Symbol	Multiples and Sub-Multiples		
kilolitre	kL	= 1 000 L =	1 000 000 mL =	10^6 mL
hectolitre	hL	= 100 L =	100 000 mL =	10^5 mL
decalitre	daL	= 10 L =	10 00 mL =	10^4 mL
litre	L	= 1 L =	1 000 mL =	10^3 mL
decilitre	dL	= 0,1 L =	100 mL =	10^2 mL
centilitre	cL	= 0,01 L =	10 mL =	10^1 mL
millilitre	mL	= 0,001 L =	1 mL =	10^0 mL

kL	hL	daL	L	dL	cL	mL	μL
1	10^1	10^2	10^3	10^4	10^5	10^6	10^9
	1	10^1	10^2	10^3	10^4	10^5	10^8
		1	10^1	10^2	10^3	10^4	10^7
			1	10^1	10^2	10^3	10^6
				1	10^1	10^2	10^5
					1	10^1	10^4
						1	10^3

μL	mL	cL	dL	L	daL	hL	kL
1	10^{-3}	10^{-4}	10^{-5}	10^{-6}	10^{-7}	10^{-8}	10^{-9}
	1	10^{-1}	10^{-2}	10^{-3}	10^{-4}	10^{-5}	10^{-6}
		1	10^{-1}	10^{-2}	10^{-3}	10^{-4}	10^{-5}
			1	10^{-1}	10^{-2}	10^{-3}	10^{-4}
				1	10^{-1}	10^{-2}	10^{-3}
					1	10^{-1}	10^{-2}
						1	10^{-1}

1 μL (microlitre) = 1 mm^3 (cubic millimetre)
1 mL (millilitre) = 1 cm^3 (cubic centimetre)
1 L (litre)   = 1 dm^3 (cubic decimetre)
1 kL   = 1 m^3 (cubic metre)

The capacity of a container is measured in litres or, if the capacity is large, in cubic metres or kilolitres

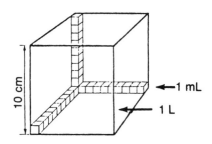

$$10 \text{ cm} \times 10 \text{ cm} \times 10 \text{ cm} = 1\ 000 \text{ cm}^3 = 1\ 000 \text{ mL}$$
$$1 \text{ L} = 1 \text{ dm}^3 = 1 \text{ kg of water}$$

Capacity calculations in SI units
Example 1

What is the volume of a cube measuring 100 mm on a side?
Express your answer in cubic centimetres and millilitres.

$$
\begin{aligned}
(100 \text{ mm})^3 &= 1\ 000\ 000 \text{ mm}^3 &= 10^6 \text{ mm}^3 \\
&= 1\ 000 \text{ cm}^3 &= 10^3 \text{ cm}^3 \\
1\ 000 \text{ cm}^3 &= 1\ 000 \text{ mL} &= 10^3 \text{ mL}
\end{aligned}
$$

Example 2

A cubic container measuring 1 kL (kilolitre) is filled with water to a line
50 cm (centimetres) from the top of the container. Express the volume
of water in cubic decimetres (dm^3) and litres (L) and its mass in kilograms (kg) and megagrams (Mg).

$$
\begin{aligned}
1 \text{ kL} &= 1 \text{ m}^3 \\
1 \text{ m}^3 &= 1\ 000 \text{ dm}^3 \\
&= 1\ 000 \text{ L}
\end{aligned}
$$

Since the container is only half-filled with water, the volume and mass
of water are as follows:

$$
\begin{aligned}
&500 \text{ dm}^3 \text{ and } 500 \text{ L} \\
&500 \text{ kg and } 0.5 \text{ Mg}
\end{aligned}
$$

Additional examples of calculations in SI units

Acceleration – F = ma
F = force in N
m = mass in kg
a = acceleration in m / s^2

What force is required to accelerate a mass of 20 kg at a rate of 4 m / s^2 ?
20 kg × 4 m / s^2 = 80 N

Acceleration (angular)
A flywheel is given a speed of 900 r / min in 15 s. Determine the angular acceleration in rad / s^2, and the linear acceleration of a point 3 m from the axis?

angular speed of 900 r / min	=	15 r / s × 2 π rad / r
	=	30 π rad / s
angular acceleration	=	gain of angular speed / time taken
	=	30 π rad / s ÷ 15 s = 2 π rad / s^2
linear acceleration	=	2 π rad / s^2 × 3 m = 6 π m / s^2

Acceleration (gravity)
A steel ball dropped from a tower strikes the ground in 3 s. Determine the height of the tower?
The acceleration "g" of any free falling body is 9,80 m / s^2
h = 1 / 2 gt^2 = 1/2 × 9.80 m / s^2 × (3 s)^2 = 44.1 m

(See also weight).

Acceleration (linear)
A train's speed increases uniformly from 36 km / h to 72 km / h in 5 min. Determine the average speed, the distance travelled, and the acceleration?

36 km / h = 10 m / s
72 km / h = 20 m / s

average speed	=	1/2 (10 + 20) = 15 m / s
distance	=	average speed × time.
	=	15 m / s × 300 s = 4 500 m
acceleration	=	change in speed / time taken for change
	=	(20 − 10) m / s ÷ 300 s = 0.0333 m / s^2

Atmospheric pressure
Example 1
A balloon has a capacity of 1 000 m^3. Find its lifting force when filled with helium. Average density of air is 1.25 g / L; helium = 0.178 g / L
lifting force = mass of displaced air minus mass of contained gas.
1 000 m^3 = 1 000 000 L
mass of displaced air = 10^6 L × 1.25 g / L = 1 250 kg
mass of helium in balloon = 10^6 × 0.178 g / L = 178 kg
lifting force of helium balloon is:
1 250 kg − 178 kg = 1 072 kg = 10.52 kN

Example 2
A barometer reads 760 mmHg at the bottom of a tower, and 757 at the top of the tower. Determine the height of the tower. Assume that the average density of the air, there, is 0.001 2 g / cm^3. Density of mercury is 13.6 g / cm^3
Change of pressure of the air = height of tower × density of air.
(76 − 75.7) cm × 13.6 g / cm^3 = h × 0.001 2 g / cm^3
h = 0.3 cm × 13.6 ÷ 0.001 2 = 3 400 cm = 34 m

Centrifugal force

A mass of 5 kg revolves with an angular speed of 40 rad / s at the end of a rope 4 m long. What is the centrifugal force produced?

$5 \times (40)^2 \times 4 = 32\ 000\ (kg{\cdot}m) / s^2 = 32\ kN$

Concentration
Example 1

Express 240 lb / ft³ in kg / m³

1 lb = 0.453 6 kg

1 ft³ = 0.028 316 m³

$\dfrac{240 \times 0{,}453\ 6}{0.028\ 316} = 3\ 844\ kg / m^3$

Example 2

Express 1 lb / (CAN) gal in kg / m³

1 lb = 0.453 6 kg

1 gal = 0.004 546 09 m³

$\dfrac{1 \times 0.453\ 6}{0.004\ 546\ 09} = 99.78\ kg / m^3$

Density
Example 1

A litre of milk weighs 1 032 g. The butterfat which it contains to the extent of 4% by volume has a density of 0.865 g / mL. What is the density of the fat free "skimmed" milk?

volume of fat in a litre of milk = 4% × 1 000 mL = 40 mL of fat.

mass of 40 mL of fat = 40 mL × 0.865 g / mL = 35 g

(1 032 − 35) g = 997 g

(1 000 − 40) mL = 960 mL

density = 997 g ÷ 960 mL = 1.039 g / mL

Example 2

A sample of ceramic material 40 mm × 25 mm × 15 mm weighs 32.3 g. What is its density?

volume = 40 × 25 × 15 mm³ = 15 cm³

density = 32.3 g ÷ 15 cm³ = 2.15 g / cm³ = 2 150 kg / m³

Electricity

Ohm's law tells us that the current flow in amperes is directly proportional to the applied electromotive force (emf) in volts and inversely proportional to the resistance in ohms.

I = E / R (I = ampere, E = volt, R = ohm)

since E = IR, IE = I × IR = I²R

Example 1

An electric heater of 8 Ω uses 15 A of current. Determine the rate at which heat is developed in watts. What is the cost of operating the heater for 4 hours at 5 cents per kW·h?

$W \times I^2R = (15\ A)^2 \times 8\ \Omega = 1\ 800\ W$

1.8 kW × 4 h × 5 cents / kW·h = 36 cents

Example 2

A current of 5 A passes through a 20 Ω electric iron. Calculate the heat energy in joules developed in 30 s?

$$\begin{aligned}
J = I^2R &= (5\ A)^2 \times 20\ \Omega \times 30\ s \\
&= 15\ 000\ J \\
&= 15\ kJ
\end{aligned}$$

Example 3
An electric motor uses 12 A at 200 V to operate a hoist that lifts 1 t or Mg at the rate of 8 m / min. Determine the energy in joules and the kilowatt-hours consumed in 30 min.

watts suplied to motor =   12 A × 200 V
                        =   2 400 W
                        =   2.4 kW
joules = 2 400 W × 1 800 s =   4 320 000 W·s
                            =   4 320 000 J
                            =   4.32 MJ
kilowatt-hours =   2.4 kW × 1/2 h = 1.2 kW·h

Electromagnetic force
A conductor 1 m long, carries a current of 2 000 A in a magnetic field whose flux density is 1.6 T. What is the force on the conductor?
1 × 2 000 × 1.6 = 3 200 N

Energy
Energy is the capacity to do work. Heat is potential or expended energy. Work is the required or expended energy to move a force a specific distance.

$$1 \text{ J} = 1 \text{ W·s} = 1 \text{ N·m}$$

The standard SI unit of energy is the joule (J). The mechanical definition of the joule is that it is the work done when a force of 1 N moves a distance of 1 m in the direction of its application.

The electrical unit of energy is the kilowatt-hour (kW·h), which is equal to $3.6 × 10^6$ J. It will eventually be replaced by the megajoule (MJ).

The watt (W) is the power which gives rise to the production of energy at the rate of 1 J / s (Joule per second).

The kilojoule (kJ) replaces the British thermal unit (Btu) as the unit of measure for quantity of heat, heat capacity etc.

1 Btu = 1.055 kJ
1 kJ = 0.948 Btu

Example:
Express 1 Btu / (ft²·min) in W / m²
1 Btu / min = 17.581 W
1 ft² = 0.092 903 m²
1 × 17.581 W ÷ 0.092 903 m² = 189.2 W / m²

Energy and Heat
Heat units

quantity of heat	joule (J)
heat flow rate	watt (J / s)
heat capacity	joules per kelvin (J / K)
combustion intensity	watts per cubic metre (W / m³)
heat flux	watts per square metre (W / m²)
heat transfer coefficient	watts per square metre kelvin W / (m²·K)
specific energy	joules per kelvin (J / K)
specific heat energy	joules per kilogram kelvin J / (kg·K)

Example
A steam boiler is fired with oil having a calorific value of 35 MJ / kg. What is the equivalent energy content of a kilogram of the oil expressed in kilowatt-hours?
1 W·s = 1 J, 1 W·h = 3 600 J, 1 kW·h = 3.6 MJ
(35 / 3.6) MJ = 9.72 kW·h

Energy and Work
Energy = force × distance = work done

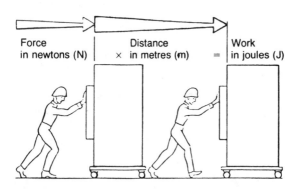

| Force in newtons (N) | × | Distance in metres (m) | = | Work in joules (J) |

Example 1
Find the work done when a mass of 25 kg is moved a distance of 20 m against the force of gravity?
Work = force × distance
     = (25 kg × 9.80 m / s^2) × 20 m
     = 4 900 J = 4.9 kJ

Example 2
Find the work done when a 600 kg steel beam is raised from ground level to the top of a building 20 m high?
Force of gravity in newtons = 600 kg × 9.80 m / s^2 = 5 880 N
5 880 N × 20 m = 117 600 J × 117.6 kJ

Example 3
What is the work done by a force of 5 kN when it moves a distance of 4 m?
Force in newtons × distance in metres = work in joules
5 kN × 4 m = 20 kJ

Example 4
What is the effective work done if 15 kL of water is pumped through a height of 20 m? The work is done against gravity and hence, since the mass of 1 L of water is 1 kg for all practical purposes,
work done = 15 × 1 000 kg × 9.81 m / s^2 × 20 m
          = 2 943 000 kg·m^2 / s^2 or J
          = 2.943 MJ

Flow rate (volume basis)
Express 1 cubic foot per second (ft^3 / s) in cubic decimetres per minute (dm^3 / min).
1 ft^3 = 28.316 dm^3
1 s = 0.016 666 min

$$\frac{1 \times 28.316}{0.016\ 666} = 1699 \text{ dm}^3 / \text{min}$$

Force

The SI unit of force is the newton (N). The newton is a very small force, it is the force required to give a mass of 1 kilogram, an acceleration of 1 metre per second squared.

$$\begin{aligned} \text{Force} \ &= \ \text{mass} \times \text{acceleration} \\ &= \ 1 \text{ kg} \times 9.81 \text{ m}/\text{s}^2 \\ &= \ 9.81 \text{ N} \end{aligned}$$

Whenever a force is applied in opposition to gravity, g must be considered.

[g (acceleration due to gravity) $= 9.81$ m$/$s^2]

In this case we express the force as 9.81 newtons, not 1 kilogram.

$1 \text{ N} = 1 \text{ J}/\text{m} = 1 \text{ kg}{\cdot}\text{m}/\text{s}^2$

Note: 9.81 N is also the force needed to keep the mass of 1 kg suspended in space.

Example 1

A net force causes a mass of 40 kg to be accelerated at 12 m$/$s^2. What is the value of the force?

$40 \text{ kg} \times 12 \text{ m}/\text{s}^2 = 480 \text{ N}$

Example 2

A force of 150 N is applied to a mass of 50 kg. What will be the acceleration on the 50 kg body?

$150 \text{ N}/50 \text{ kg} = 3 \text{ m}/\text{s}^2$

Example 3

A force of 1 200 N acts for 12 s to change the velocity of a rocket from 600 m$/$s to 2 300 m$/$s. What is the mass of the rocket?

$(2\ 300 - 600) \text{ m}/\text{s} = 1\ 700 \text{ m}/\text{s}$

$$\frac{1\ 200 \text{ N} \times 12 \text{ s}}{1\ 700 \text{ m}/\text{s}} = 8.47 \text{ kg}$$

Example 4

A force of 1 MN is required to give a locomotive an acceleration of 5 m$/$s^2. Express the mass (wt) of the locomotive in tonnes (t) and megagrams (Mg).

$1 \text{ MN} = 10^6 \text{ N}$

$$\frac{1\ 000\ 000 \text{ N}}{5 \text{ m}/\text{s}^2} = 200\ 000 \text{ kg} = 200 \text{ t} = 200 \text{ Mg}$$

Gases

The familiar law for 1 mole of ideal gas is $PV = RT$

R, the gas constant has the value, 8.31 J$/$(mol$\cdot$K)

What mass of CO_2 at 27°C occupies 3 m^3 at a pressure of 10 kN$/$m^2?

$PV = nRT$

$P = 10 \text{ kN}/\text{m}^2$, $V = 3 \text{ m}^3$, $T = (27 + 273) \text{ K}$

hence, $n \ = \ \dfrac{10 \times 1\ 000 \times 3}{8.31 \times 300} \ = \ 12 \text{ mol}$

and mass $\ = \ 12 \times 44 = 528 \text{ g}$

Heat and Thermodynamics
Example 1
Two furnace oil quotations are received. While the price per kilolitre (tonne or cubic metre) is the same for each, oil A is specified as having a calorific value of 19 230 Btu / lb, while oil B is rated at 44.82 MJ / kg. Which oil is the better buy?

$$1 \text{ Btu} = 1\ 055.06 \text{ J}$$
$$1 \text{ Btu} / \text{lb} = 2.326 \text{ J} / \text{g} = 2.326 \text{ kJ} / \text{kg}$$
$$19\ 230 \times 2.326 \qquad = 44\ 729 \text{ kJ} / \text{kg}$$
$$\qquad\qquad\qquad\qquad = 44.729 \text{ MJ} / \text{kg}$$

Oil B with 44.82 MJ / kg is the better buy.

Example 2
For solids and liquids the energy increment corresponding to a given temperature change is usually given in joule per kilogram per kelvin. This quantity is the specific heat or thermal capacity.
Here are typical values, obtained experimentally:

water	4 190 J / (kg·K)
ice	2 100 J / (kg·K)
copper	300 J / (kg·K)
steel	404 J / (kg·K)

Values are usually measured at 15°C, and may vary considerably with temperature and pressure.

A litre of boiling water is poured into an unwarmed stainless steel teapot of mass 250 g, initially at a temperature of 15°C. At what temperature does the tea begin to brew?
Taking the tabulated values:
initial energy level above 0°C
$$= (4\ 190 \times 100) + (0.25 \times 404 \times 15) \text{ J}$$

final energy level above 0°C
$$[4\ 190 + (0.25 \times 404)] \times T \text{ joule}$$

Where T is the final temperature in degrees, Hence, assuming no losses have occured,
$$T = 419\ 000 + 1500 \div 4190 + 101 \times 98°C$$

Illumination
The basic unit of luminous intensity is the candela. One candela will produce a luminous flux of one lumen within a solid angle of one steradian.
$$1 \text{ cd} = 1 \text{ lm} / \text{sr}$$
One lumen is the flux emitted in a cone of solid angle of one steradian by a special point source of uniform intensity of one candela.

$$1 \text{ lm} = 1 \text{ cd·sr}$$
One lux is the even illumination (or illuminance) of one lumen over an area of one square metre.
$$1 \text{ lx} = 1 \text{ lm} / \text{m}^2 = 1 \text{ cd·sr} / \text{m}^2$$

Example 1
What is the luminous flux when a luminous intensity of 20 cd is generated within a solid angle of 0.4 sr?
$$20 \text{ cd} / 0.4 \text{ sr} = 50 \text{ lm}$$

Example 2
What must be the solid angle enclosing a light source capable of generating 35 cd if it is to be rated at 140 lm?
35 cd / 140 lm = 0.25 sr

Example 3
A lighting fixture delivers 20 klm to a surface of 15 m². What is the illumination rating of the fixture in lux?
20 klm / 15 m² = 1.33 klx

Impact
A mass of 4 kg moving at a speed of 20 m / s, is brought to a stop in 0.1 s. What is the average force of impact?
4 × 20 ÷ 0.1 = 800 N

Induced electromotive force (emf)
What is the voltage induced in a conductor of 1 m long, moving with a velocity of 20 m / s through a magnetic field whose flux density is 1.6 T?
1 × 20 × 1.6 = 32 V
Solution expressed in terms of base units is as follows:
1 m × 20 m/s × 1.6 kg / (s²·A) = 32 m²·kg / (s³·A)
                                 = 32 V

Kinetic energy
What is the kinetic energy of an automobile having a mass of 2 000 kg, moving at a speed of 15 m / s?
$E = 1/2\ mv^2 = 1/2 \times 2\ 000 \times 225 = 225\ 000$ J
                                              = 225 kJ

Moment of inertia
Calculate the moment of inertia of a disc with a radius of 0.8 m and a mass of 50 kg?
$50 \times (0.8)^2 \div 2 = 16$ kg·m²

Momentum
What is the momentum of a mass of 10 kg moving at a velocity of 10 m / s?
10 × 10 = 100 kg·m / s = 100 N·s

Motor power
A motor produces a torque of 4 N·m while turning at an angular speed of 50 rad / s. What is the mechanical power developed?
50 × 4 N·m / s = 200 W

Power
The basic unit of power is the watt. It is the [SI] unit for all forms of power; heat, electrical, mechanical, etc. A watt is energy per unit time, measured in joules per second (J / s). This derived unit has been given the special name of watt.

Example 1
How many watts are required to produce 480 J in 8 s?
(1 W = 1 J / s). 480 J in 8 s = 60 W

Example 2
How many watts are consumed in lifting 50 kg through a height of 20 m in 1 min?
Power in watts = work in joules / time in seconds
               = 50 kg × 9.80 m / s² = 490 N
                 490 N × 20 m × 9 800 J
                 9 800 J in 60 s × 163 W

Pressure

Example 1
What is the stress in a 20 mm diameter steel wire
used to lift a mass of 1 tonne (t)?

$0,7854 \times D^2$ = area of wire
$0,7854 \times 400$ mm = 314,16 mm²

$$\frac{314,16 \text{ mm}^2}{1\ 000\ 000 \text{ mm}^2} = 0,000\ 314\ 16 \text{ m}^2$$

1 t = 1000 kg × 9,81 m/s²
   = 9810 (kg·m)/s²
   = 9810 N

$$\frac{9810 \text{ N}}{0,000\ 314\ 16 \text{ m}^2} = 31\ 142\ 857 \text{ N/m}^2$$
$$= 31\ 142,8 \text{ kN/m}^2$$
$$= 31,1 \text{ MN/m}^2 \text{ (MPa) (ans.)}.$$

Example 2
When this hot water boiler is heated the hot water
exerts a force of 600 kilonewtons over a surface
area of 2 square metres. What pressure is created? (express unit as a symbol)

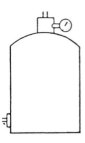

$$\text{pressure} = \frac{\text{force}}{\text{area}}$$
$$= \frac{600 \times 1000 \text{ N}}{2 \text{ m}^2}$$
$$= \frac{300 \text{ kN}}{\text{m}^2} = 300 \text{ kPa (ans.)}.$$

Remember: 1 N/m² = 1 Pa
          1 kN/m² = 1 kPa
          1 MN/m² = 1 MPa

Example 3
If a force of 1 kN is exerted on a wire of cross-
section area 200 mm² what will be the stress
(pressure) on the wire? (express unit as a symbol)

Note: take care to convert kN to N and mm² to m²
when you work this one out.

$$\text{stress} = \frac{\text{force}}{\text{area}}$$

$$= \frac{1000 \text{ N}}{200 / 10^{-6} \text{ m}^2}$$

$$= 5 \times 10^6 \text{ Pa}$$
$$= 5 \text{ MPa (MN/m}^2\text{) (ans.)}.$$

TABLE 9 — EQUIVALENT SI UNITS 141

1 ampere	(A)	= 1 C/s
1 ampere hour	(A·h)	= 3 600 C = 3.6 kC
1 ampere per volt	(A/V)	= 1 S
1 ampere per weber	(A/Wb)	= 1/H or H⁻¹
1 becquerel	(Bq)	= 1/s or s⁻¹
1 candela	(cd)	= 1 lm/sr
1 candela steradian	(cd·sr)	= 1 lm
1 candela steradian per sq. metre	(cd·sr/m²)	= 1 lx
1 coulomb	(C)	= 1 A·s
1 coulomb per volt	(C/V)	= 1 F
1 farad	(F)	= 1 C/V
1 gray	(Gy)	= 1 J/kg
1 gray per second	(Gy/s)	= 1 W/kg
1 henry	(H)	= 1 Wb/A
1 hertz	(Hz)	= 1/s or s⁻¹
1 joule	(J)	= 1 N·m
1 joule per ampere second	[J/(A·s)]	= 1 V
1 joule per kilogram second	[J/(kg·s)]	= 1 W/kg
1 joule per second	(J/s)	= 1 W
1 joule per tesla	(J/T)	= 1 A·m²
1 kilolitre	(kL)	= 1 m³ or t
1 kilopascal	(kPa)	= 1 kN/m²
1 kilowatt	(kW)	= 3,6 MJ/h or 1 000 J/s
1 kilowatt hour	(kW·h)	= 3,6 MJ
1 lumen	(lm)	= 1 cd·sr
1 lumen per square metre	(lm/m²)	= 1 lx
1 lux	(lx)	= 1 lm/m²
1 newton metre	(N·m)	= 1 J
1 newton per coulomb	(N/C)	= 1 V/m
1 newton per metre	(N/m)	= 1 J/m²
1 newton second per sq. metre	(N·s/m²)	= 1 Pa·s
1 ohm	(Ω)	= 1 H/s
1 ohm second	(Ω·s)	= 1 H
1 ohm, reciprocal	(Ω⁻¹)	= 1 S
1 pascal	(Pa)	= 1 N/m²
1 rad	(rad or rd)	= 0,01 Gy
1 siemens	(S)	= 1 A/V
1 sievert	(Sv)	= 1 J/kg
1 square metre per newton	(m²/N)	= Pa⁻¹
1 tesla	(T)	= 1 Wb/m²
1 tonne	(t)	= 1 Mg or m³ or kL
1 volt	(V)	= 1 W/A
1 volt ampere	(V·A)	= 1 W
1 volt per ampere	(V/A)	= 1 Ω
1 volt second	(V·s)	= 1 Wb
1 volt second per ampere	(V·s/A)	= 1 H
1 volt second per sq. metre	(V·s/m²)	= 1 T
1 watt	(W)	= 1 J/s or V/A
1 watt hour	(W·h)	= 3,6 kJ
1 watt per ampere	(W/A)	= 1 V
1 watt second	(W·s)	= 1 J
1 weber	(Wb)	= 1 V·s
1 weber per ampere	(Wb/A)	= 1 H
1 weber per sq. metre	(Wb/m²)	= 1 T

absolute gravity	$\times$ 9,812 60	= m/s^2
acceleration of free fall	$\times$ 9,806 65	= m/s^2
atomic mass constant	$\times$ 1,660 565 $\times$ 10^{-27}	= kg
Avogadro constant	$\times$ 6,022 045 $\times$ 10^{23}	= mol^{-1}
Bohr magneton	$\times$ 9,274 078 $\times$ 10^{-24}	= J/T
Bohr radius	$\times$ 0,529 177 $\times$ 10^{-10}	= m
Boltzmann constant	$\times$ 1,380 622 $\times$ 10^{-23}	= J/K
constant in Ampere's circ. law	$\times$ 2 $\quad\times$ 10^{-7}	= N/A^2
constant in Coulomb's law	$\times$ 8,988 $\quad\times$ 10^9	= N·m^2/C^2
constant in Kepler's law	$\times$ 3,335 $\quad\times$ 10^{18}	= m^3/s^2
constant relating wavenumber with energy	$\times$ 1,196 255 $\times$ 10^{-1}	= J·m/mol
earth, equatorial radius	$\times$ 6,378 160 $\times$ 10^6	= m
Einstein constant relating mass and energy	$\times$ 8,987 554 $\times$ 10^{16}	= J/kg
electronvolt	$\times$ 1,602 1 $\quad\times$ 10^{-19}	= J
electron charge, specific	$\times$ 1,758 805 $\times$ 10^{11}	= C/kg
electron radius	$\times$ 2,817 938 $\times$ 10^{-15}	= m
electron rest mass	$\times$ 0,910 953 $\times$ 10^{-30}	= kg
	$\times$ 5,485 803 $\times$ 10^{-4}	= u
elementary charge	$\times$ 1,602 189 $\times$ 10^{-19}	= C
Faraday constant	$\times$ 9,648 456 $\times$ 10^4	= C/mol
first radiation constant	$\times$ 3,741 832 $\times$ 10^{-16}	= W·m^2
gas constant, (molar)	$\times$ 8,314 41	= J/(mol·K)
gravitational constant	$\times$ 6,672 $\quad\times$ 10^{-11}	= N·m^2/kg^2
Josephson frequency-voltage ratio	$\times$ 483,593 9	= T·Hz/V
magnetic flux quantum	$\times$ 2,067 851 $\times$ 10^{-15}	= Wb
magnetic moment of electron	$\times$ 9,284 832 $\times$ 10^{-24}	= J/T
magnetic moment of proton	$\times$ 1,410 617 $\times$ 10^{-26}	= J/T
molar volume, ideal gas (273,15 K, 101,325 kPa)	$\times$ 0,022 414	= m^3/mol
neutron rest mass	$\times$ 1,674 954 $\times$ 10^{-27}	= kg
permeability of vacuum	$\times$ 12,566 37 $\times$ 10^{-7}	= H/m
permittivity of vacuum	$\times$ 8,854 188 $\times$ 10^{-12}	= F/m
Plank constant, chemistry	$\times$ 3,993 547 $\times$ 10^{-34}	= J·s/mol
Plank constant, physics	$\times$ 6,626 176 $\times$ 10^{-34}	= J·s
proton gyromagnetic ratio	$\times$ 2,675 199 $\times$ 10^8	= s^{-1}·T^{-1}
proton rest mass	$\times$ 1,672 649 $\times$ 10^{-27}	= kg
Rydberg constant	$\times$ 1,097 373 $\times$ 10^7	= m^{-1}
second radiation constant	$\times$ 0,014 388	= m·K
Stefan-Boltzmann constant	$\times$ 5,670 32 $\quad\times$ 10^{-8}	= W/(m^2·K^4)
velocity of light in vacuum	$\times$ 299 792 458	= m/s
velocity of sound in air	$\times$ 332	= m/s

TABLE 11 — METRIC CONVERSION TABLE   143

The convenient table on the following page provides a fast and easy means of conversion from one metric notation to another for all units; base units, supplementary units, and derived units. This table may also be used to find units of area and volume as explained below.

The value labelled "Unit" represents the basic unit such as metre, gram, ampere, watt, etc. First, locate the original or given value in the left-hand column, and follow this line horizontally to the vertical column headed by the prefix of the desired value. The figure and sign at this intersection indicate the direction in which the decimal point or comma should be moved and the number of places to move it. The plus sign (+) is moved to the right and the minus sign (−) to the left. Simply remember this — when you are working from a base unit to smaller units, move the decimal marker to the right. When you are working from the base unit to larger units, move the decimal marker to the left. Examples;

1. **Convert 0,15 megavolt to volts.** Starting in the "Mega" box in the left-hand column, move horizontally to the column headed by "Unit" (since volt is a basic unit of measurement), and read (+ 6). Thus, 0,15 MV is the equivalent of 150 000 V.

2. **Convert 1 000 milliwatts to megawatt.** Read in the box horizontal to "milli' and under "mega" the notation (− 9), which means a shift of the decimal marker 9 places to the left. Thus 1 000 mW is the equivalent of 0,000 001 or 10^{-6} MW.

3. **Convert 4 500 kilohertz to megahertz.** Read in the box horizontal to "kilo" and under "Mega" the notation (− 3), which means a shift of the decimal point 3 places to the left. Thus 4 500 kHz is the equivalent of 4,5 MHz.

Note: if you are working with area (some measure squared) or with capacity (some measure cubed) remember that you must multiply the (−) or (+) exponents in the table by 2 or 3 respectively.
Examples:

4. **Convert 1 square metre to square millimetre and 1 cubic metre to cubic millimetres.**
   1 m   = 10^3 mm (straight measure)
   1 m² = 10^6 mm² (square measure)
   1 m³ = 10^9 mm³ (cubic measure)

5. **Convert 1 000 000 cm³ to m³**
   1 000 000 cm³   = 10^6 cm³
                   = 10^4 cm² × 10^2 cm
                   =   1 m² × 1 m
                   =   1 m³

Metric conversion table

Original Value	Desired Value																
	Exa-	Peta-	Tera-	Giga-	Mega-	Kilo-	Hecto-	Deca-	Unit	Deci-	Centi-	Milli-	Micro-	Nano-	Pico-	Femto-	Atto-
Exa-		+3	+6	+9	+12	+15	+16	+17	+18	+19	+20	+21	+24	+27	+30	+33	+36
Peta-	-3		+3	+6	+9	+12	+13	+14	+15	+16	+17	+18	+21	+24	+27	+30	+33
Tera-	-6	-3		+3	+6	+9	+10	+11	+12	+13	+14	+15	+18	+21	+24	+27	+30
Giga-	-9	-6	-3		+3	+6	+7	+8	+9	+10	+11	+12	+15	+18	+21	+24	+27
Mega-	-12	-9	-6	-3		+3	+4	+5	+6	+7	+8	+9	+12	+15	+18	+21	+24
Kilo-	-15	-12	-9	-6	-3		+1	+2	+3	+4	+5	+6	+9	+12	+15	+18	+21
Hecto-	-16	-13	-10	-7	-4	-1		+1	+2	+3	+4	+5	+8	+11	+14	+17	+20
Deca-	-17	-14	-11	-8	-5	-2	-1		+1	+2	+3	+4	+7	+10	+13	+16	+19
Unit	-18	-15	-12	-9	-6	-3	-2	-1		+1	+2	+3	+6	+9	+12	+15	+18
Deci-	-19	-16	-13	-10	-7	-4	-3	-2	-1		+1	+2	+5	+8	+11	+14	+17
Centi-	-20	-17	-14	-11	-8	-5	-4	-3	-2	-1		+1	+4	+7	+10	+13	+16
Milli-	-21	-18	-15	-12	-9	-6	-5	-4	-3	-2	-1		+3	+6	+9	+12	+15
Micro-	-24	-21	-18	-15	-12	-9	-8	-7	-6	-5	-4	-3		+3	+6	+9	+12
Nano-	-27	-24	-21	-18	-15	-12	-11	-10	-9	-8	-7	-6	-3		+3	+6	+9
Pico-	-30	-27	-24	-21	-18	-15	-14	-13	-12	-11	-10	-9	-6	-3		+3	+6
Femto-	-33	-30	-27	-24	-21	-18	-17	-16	-15	-14	-13	-12	-9	-6	-3		+3
Atto-	-36	-33	-30	-27	-24	-21	-20	-19	-18	-17	-16	-15	-12	-9	-6	-3	

TABLE 12 — TEMPERATURE 145

The following table shows the various temperature scales. With the SI, only the kelvin and the Celsius scales are accepted.

Conversion formulas

degree Celsius (°C)	= (°F −32) × 5/9 = (°Re × 5/4) = (K − 273,15)
degree Fahrenheit (°F)	= (°C × 9/5) + 32 = (°Re × 9/4) + 32 = (1,8 × K) −459,67
kelvin (K)	= (°C + 273,15) = (°F + 459,67) ÷ 1,8 = (°R ÷ 1,8)
degree Rankine (°R)	= (°F + 459,67) = (K × 1,8)
degree Réaumur (°Re)	= (°F − 32) × 4/9

Scale comparison

Temperature		Kelvin	Celsius	Fahrenheit
boiling point of water	=	373,15	100	212
freezing point of water	=	273,15	0	32
absolute zero	=	0	−273,15	−459,67

Note: The thermodynamic temperature of the triple point of water is 273,16 K or 0,01 °C.

Examples of temperature conversion

100 °C	= (100 × 1,8) °F + 32 = 212 °F
25 °C	= (25 + 273,15) °C = 298,15 K
120 K	= (273,15 −120) K = 153,15 °C
212 °F	= (212 −32) °F ÷ 1,8 = 100 °C
212 °F	= (212 + 459,67) °F ÷ 1,8 = 373,15 K
80 °Re	= (80 × 1,25) °C = 100 °C

Temperature difference

1 °F	= 0,555 6 °C	= 0,555 6 K
1 °C	= 1,8 °F	= 1 K
1 K	= 1 °C	= 1,8 °F

The unit of temperature for common use is the degree Celsius. The centigrade term is not used to avoid confusion with the word centigrade associated with angular measure. The kelvin scale (sometimes called the absolute scale) is very useful in science, for instance, in the study of gas laws. There are no negative readings on the kelvin scale since the lowest temperature, −273,15 °C is called zero kelvin or absolute zero. The kelvin scale is named after Sir William Thompson, Lord Kelvin, British scientist, (1824-1907). His scale is nothing more than the Celsius scale as far as ratio is concerned. 1 K = 1 °C.

The central figures refer to the temperatures, either in degrees Celsius or in degrees Fahrenheit, which require conversion. The corresponding temperatures in degrees Fahrenheit or degrees Celsius will be found to the right or left respectively.

°C		°F	°C		°F
− 17,8	0	32,0			
− 17,2	1	33,8	10,6	51	123,8
− 16,7	2	35,6	11,1	52	125,6
− 16,1	3	37,4	11,7	53	127,4
− 15,6	4	39,2	12,2	54	129,2
− 15,0	5	41,0	12,8	55	131,0
− 14,4	6	42,8	13,3	56	132,8
− 13,9	7	44,6	13,9	57	134,6
− 13,3	8	46,4	14,4	58	136,4
− 12,8	9	48,2	15,0	59	138,2
− 12,2	10	50.0	15,6	60	140,0
− 11,7	11	51,8	16,1	61	141,8
− 11,1	12	53,6	16,7	62	143,6
− 10,6	13	55,4	17,2	63	145,4
− 10,0	14	57,2	17,8	64	147,2
− 9,4	15	59,0	18,3	65	149,0
− 8,9	16	60,8	18,9	66	150,8
− 8,3	17	62,6	19,4	67	152,6
− 7,8	18	64,4	20,0	68	154,4
− 7,2	19	66,2	20,6	69	156,2
− 6,7	20	68,0	21,1	70	158,0
− 6,1	21	69,8	21,7	71	159,8
− 5,6	22	71,6	22,2	72	161,6
− 5,0	23	73,4	22,8	73	163,4
− 4,4	24	75,2	23,3	74	165,2
− 3,9	25	77,0	23,9	75	167,0
− 3,3	26	78,8	24,4	76	168,8
− 2,8	27	80,6	25,0	77	170,6
− 2,2	28	82,4	25,6	78	172,4
− 1,7	29	84,2	26,1	79	174,2
− 1,1	30	86,0	26,7	80	176,0
− 0,6	31	87,8	27,2	81	177,8
0,0	32	89,6	27,8	82	179,6
0,6	33	91,4	28,3	83	181,4
1,1	34	93,2	28,9	84	183,2
1,7	35	95,0	29,4	85	185,0
2,2	36	96,8	30,0	86	186,8
2,8	37	98,6	30,6	87	188,6
3,3	38	100,4	31,1	88	190,4
3,9	39	102,2	31,7	89	192,2
4,4	40	104,0	32,2	90	194,0
5,0	41	105,8	32,8	91	195,8
5,6	42	107,6	33,3	92	197,6
6,1	43	109,4	33,9	93	199,4
6,7	44	111,2	34,4	94	201,2
7,2	45	113,0	35,0	95	203,0
7,8	46	114,8	35,6	96	204,8
8,3	47	116,6	36,1	97	206,6
8,9	48	118,4	36,7	98	208,4
9,4	49	120,2	37,2	99	210,2
10,0	50	122,0	37,8	100	212,0

TABLE 13 — FRACTIONS OF AN INCH TO MILLIMETRES 147

By manipulation of the decimal marker or comma any decimal value or multiple of an inch may be converted to its exact equivalent in millimetres.

1/2	1/4	1/8	1/16	1/32	1/64	inch	mm	
					1	0,015 625	0,397	
				1	2	0,031 25	0,794	
					3	0,046 875	1,191	
			1	2	4	0,062 5	1,588	
					5	0,078 125	1,984	
				3	6	0,093 75	2,381	
					7	0,109 375	2,778	
		1	2	4	8	0,125 0	3,175	e
					9	0,140 625	3,572	
				5	10	0,156 25	3,969	
					11	0,171 875	4,366	
			3	6	12	0,187 5	4,762	
					13	0,203 125	5,159	
				7	14	0,218 75	5,556	
					15	0,234 375	5,953	
	1	2	4	8	16	0,250 0	6,350	e
					17	0,265 625	6,747	
				9	18	0,281 25	7,144	
					19	0,296 875	7,541	
			5	10	20	0,312 5	7,938	
					21	0,328 125	8,334	
				11	22	0,343 75	8,731	
					23	0,359 375	9,128	
		3	6	12	24	0,375 0	9,525	e
					25	0,390 625	9,922	
				13	26	0,406 25	10,319	
					27	0,421 875	10,716	
			7	14	28	0,437 5	11,112	
					29	0,453 125	11,509	
				15	30	0,468 75	11,906	
					31	0,484 375	12,303	
1	2	4	8	16	32	0,500 0	12,700	e
					33	0,515 625	13,097	
				17	34	0,531 25	13,494	
					35	0,546 875	13,891	
			9	18	36	0,562 5	14,288	
					37	0,578 125	14,684	
				19	38	0,593 75	15,081	
					39	0,609 375	15,478	
			5	10	20	0,625 0	15,875	e
					41	0,640 625	16,272	
				21	42	0,656 25	16,669	
					43	0,671 875	17,066	
			11	22	44	0,687 5	17,462	
					45	0,703 125	17,859	
				23	46	0,718 75	18,256	
					47	0,734 375	18,653	
	3	6	12	24	48	0,750 0	19,050	e
					49	0,765 625	19,447	
				25	50	0,781 25	19,844	
					51	0,796 875	20,241	
			13	26	52	0,812 5	20,638	
					53	0,828 125	21,034	
				27	54	0,843 75	21,431	
					55	0,859 375	21,828	
		7	14	28	56	0,875 0	22,225	e
					57	0,809 625	22,622	
				29	58	0,906 25	23,019	
					59	0,921 875	23,416	
			15	30	60	0,937 5	23,812	
					61	0,953 125	24,209	
				31	62	0,968 75	24,606	
					63	0,984 375	25,003	
2	4	8	16	32	64	1,000 0	25,400	e

e = exact

Circumference and area of circles (millimetres).

The diameter in millimetre (mm) in the following table corresponds to the diameter in inches (in).

For example, 0.397 mm = 1 / 64 in.

To convert circumference in millimetres to circumference in inches, divide by 25.4

Example: 1.247 mm / 25.4 = 0.049 09 in

To convert area in square millimetres (mm^2) to area in square inches (in^2) divide by 645.16

Example: 0.1238 mm^2 / 645.16 = 0.000 192 in^2

Diam. in	Diam. mm	Circ. mm	Area mm^2
1 / 64	0.397	1.247	0.1238
1 / 32	0.794	2.494	0.4951
3 / 64	1.191	3.742	1.1140
1 / 16	1.587	4.985	1.9781
5 / 64	1.984	6.234	3.0915
3 / 32	2.381	7.480	4.4525
7 / 64	2.778	8.727	6.0602
1 / 8	3.175	9.974	7.9173
9 / 64	3.572	11.222	10.0169
5 / 32	3.969	12.468	12.3723
11 / 64	4.365	13.713	14.9644
3 / 16	4.763	14.963	17.8177
13 / 64	5.159	16.207	20.9036
7 / 32	5.556	17.455	24.2446
15 / 64	5.953	18.701	27.8332
1 / 4	6.350	19.949	31.6691
17 / 64	6.747	21.196	35.7529
9 / 32	7.144	22.443	40.0842
19 / 64	7.541	23.690	44.6631
5 / 16	7.937	24.935	49.4770
21 / 64	8.334	26.182	54.5503
11 / 32	8.731	27.429	59.8713
23 / 64	9.128	28.676	65.4398
3 / 8	9.525	29.923	71.2559
25 / 64	9.922	31.171	77.3196
13 / 32	10.319	32.418	83.6308
27 / 64	10.716	33.665	90.1896
3 / 8	11.112	34.909	96.9785
29 / 64	11.509	36.157	104.0318
15 / 32	11.906	37.404	111.3327
31 / 64	12.303	38.651	118.8811
1 / 2	12.700	39.898	126.6772

TABLE 13 — FRACTIONS (concluded)   149

Diam. in	Diam. mm	Circ. mm	Area mm²
33 / 64	13.097	41.114	134.7002
17 / 32	13.494	42.393	143.0119
35 / 64	13.891	43.639	151.5506
9 / 16	14.287	44.884	160.3146
37 / 64	14.684	46.131	169.3478
19 / 32	15.081	47.378	178.6286
39 / 64	15.478	48.626	188.1571
5 / 8	15.875	49.873	197.9330
41 / 64	16.272	51.120	207.9566
21 / 32	16.669	52.367	219.0402
43 / 64	17.065	53.611	228.7196
11 / 16	17.462	54.858	239.4853
45 / 64	17.858	56.106	250.4985
23 / 32	18.256	57.353	261.7593
47 / 64	18.653	58.600	273.2677
3 / 4	19.050	59.847	285.0236
49 / 64	19.447	61.094	297.0271
25 / 32	19.843	62.338	309.2471
51 / 64	20.240	63.586	321.7451
13 / 16	20.637	64.833	334.4907
53 / 64	21.034	66.080	347.4838
27 / 32	21.431	67.327	360.7246
55 / 64	21.828	68.574	374.2129
7 / 8	22.225	69.822	387.9488
57 / 64	22.621	71.065	401.8967
29 / 32	23.019	72.316	416.1633
59 / 64	23.416	73.563	430.6052
15 / 16	23.812	74.807	445.3307
61 / 64	24.209	76.054	460.3038
31 / 32	24.606	77.302	475.5245
63 / 64	25.003	78.539	490.8750
1	25.400	79.796	506.7086

By manipulation of the decimal point this table may be extended to values below 1 or above 100.

Example: 0.001 lbf / in² = 0.006 8948 kPa or 6.9848 Pa
          1000 lbf / in² = 6894.8 kPa or 6.8948 MPa
          (1 lbf / in² = psi)

lbf / in²	kPa	lbf / in²	kPa	lbf / in²	kPa
1 =	6.8948	35 =	241.3165	69 =	475.7383
2	13.7895	36	248.2113	70	482.6330
3	20.6843	37	255.1060	71	489.5278
4	27.5790	38	262.0008	72	496.4225
5	34.4738	39	268.8955	73	503.3173
6	41.3685	40	275.7903	74	510.2120
7	48.2633	41	282.6850	75	517.1068
8	55.1581	42	289.5798	76	524.0016
9	62.0528	43	296.4746	77	530.8963
10	68.9476	44	303.3693	78	537.7911
11	75.8423	45	310.2641	79	544.6858
12	82.7371	46	317.1588	80	551.5806
13	89.6318	47	324.0536	81	558.4753
14	96.5266	48	330.9484	82	565.3701
15	103.4214	49	337.8431	83	572.2649
16	110.3161	50	344.7379	84	579.1596
17	117.2109	51	351.6326	85	586.0544
18	124.1056	52	358.7274	86	592.9491
19	131.0004	53	365.4221	87	599.8439
20	137.8951	54	372.3169	88	606.7386
21	144.7899	55	379.2117	89	613.7334
22	151.6847	56	386.1064	90	620.5282
23	158.5794	57	393.0012	91	627.4229
24	165.4742	58	399.8959	92	634.3177
25	172.3689	59	406.7907	93	641.2124
26	179.2637	60	413.6854	94	648.1072
27	186.1584	61	420.5802	95	655.0019
28	193.0532	62	427.4750	96	661.8967
29	199.9480	63	434.3697	97	668.7915
30	206.8427	64	441.2645	98	675.6862
31	213.7375	65	448.1592	99	682.5810
32	220.6322	66	455.0540	100	689.4757
33	227.5250	67	461.9487		
34	234.4217	68	468.8435		

To convert 152.56 lbf / in² to kPa;

100.00 lbf / in²	=	689.4757 kPa
52.00	=	358.7274
0.56	=	3.8611
152.56	=	1056.0642

1 inch (in) = 0.0254 metre (m) exactly.
1 pound-force (lbf) = 4.448 271 615 261 newtons (N) exactly.

TABLE 15 — MENSURATION FORMULAE 151

Plane figures

RECTANGLE

Area = bh

Diagonal $D = \sqrt{b^2 + h^2}$

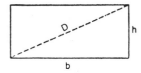

RIGHT TRIANGLE

Area $= \dfrac{ba}{2}$

Hypotenuse $= c = \sqrt{a^2 \times b^2}$

$A + B + C = 180°$

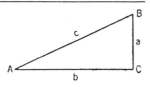

ANY TRIANGLE

Area $= \dfrac{bh}{2}$

(h is perpendicular to b)

$A + B + C = 180°$

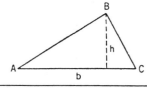

PARALLELOGRAM

(opposite sides parallel)

Area = bh

(h is perpendicular to b)

$A + B + C + D = 360°$

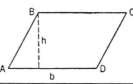

TRAPEZOID

(a parallel to b)

Area $= \left(\dfrac{a \cdot b}{2}\right) h$

(h is perpendicular to a and b)

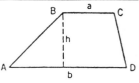

ANY REGULAR POLYGON

(Equal sides and equal angles)

Area $= \dfrac{bh}{2}$ N

(N = number of sides)

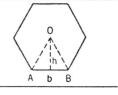

CIRCLE

Circumference $= \pi d$

$= 2 \pi r$

$\left(\pi = \dfrac{\text{circumference}}{\text{diameter}} \right)$

Area $= \pi r^2$

$= \dfrac{\pi}{4} d^2$

$= 0,7854\ d^2$

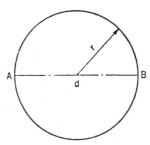

Plane figures

ELLIPSE

$$\text{Area} = \pi \, (OA)(OC)$$

$$= \frac{\pi}{4} \, (AB)(CD)$$

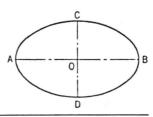

SECTOR

$$\text{Area} = \frac{r \, (\text{arc } AB)}{2}$$

$$= \frac{\pi r^2 \, (\text{angle } AOB)}{360°}$$

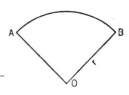

SEGMENT

$$\text{Area} = (\text{Area of sector } AOB)$$

$$- \, (\text{Area of triangle } AOB)$$

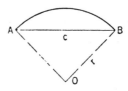

FILLET

$$\text{Area} = r^2 - \frac{\pi r^2}{4}$$

$$= 0,2146 \, r^2$$

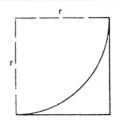

Inscribed circles
Circumscribed circles and equal squares

Diameter of circle	× 0.707 11	= side of inscribed square
" " "	× 0.886 23	= side of square of equal area
Area of circle	× 0.636 62	= area of inscribed square
" " "	× 1.273 2	= area of circumscribed square
Circumference of circle	× 1.128	= perimeter of square of equal area
Side of square	× 1.414 2	= diameter of circumscribed circle
" " "	× 4.442 8	= circumference of circumscribed circle
" " "	× 1.128	= diameter of circle of equal area
" " "	× 3.545	= circumference of circle of equal area
Perimeter of square	× 0.866	= circumference of circle of equal area

TABLE 15 — MENSURATION FORMULAE (continued)   153

Solids

SPHERE

Volume = $\dfrac{4}{3}\pi r^3 = \dfrac{\pi d^3}{6}$

Area = $4\pi r^2 = \pi d^2$

CYLINDER

Volume = $\pi r^2 L = 0,7854\, d^2 L$
Area of cylindrical surface
= πdL

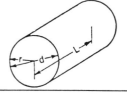

CYLINDER

Volume = (area base) h
Area of cylindrical surface
= (perimeter base) h

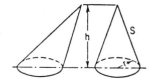

CONE

Volume (of either) = $\dfrac{1}{3}\pi r^2 h$
Area (of right cone) = πrs

FRUSTUM OF CONE

Volume = $\dfrac{1}{3}h\,(B + b + \sqrt{Bb})$

(B,b = area bases)
Volume of right cone

= $\dfrac{1}{3}h\,(\pi R^2 + \pi r^2 + \sqrt{\pi^2 R^2 r^2})$

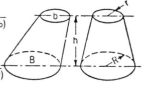

RING OR TORUS

Volume = $2\pi^2 R r^2$
Area = $4\pi^2 R r$

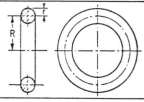

CUBE

Volume = a^3

Diagonal = $d = a\sqrt{3}$

Total area = $6a^2$

Solids

RECTANGULAR PRISM

Volume = [Area of end] C
        = a b c
Diagonal = $d = \sqrt{a^2 \cdot b^2 \cdot c^2}$
Total area = 2 [ab + bc + ca]

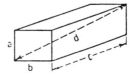

ANY PRISM

(Axis perpendicular to base or
    inclined)
  (h = perpendicular height)
Volume = (area of base) h
       = (area of perpendic-
         ular cross section)
         (length along edge)

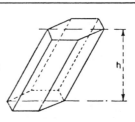

PYRAMID

Volume = $\frac{1}{3}$ (area of base) h

       = $\frac{1}{3}$ (abh)

(h perpendicular to base)

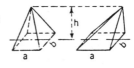

FRUSTUM OF PYRAMID

Volume = $\frac{1}{3}$ h (ab + cd + $\sqrt{(ab)(cd)}$)

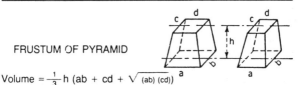

SPHERICAL SEGMENT

Volume = $\pi h^2 (r - \frac{h}{3})$

       = $\pi h (\frac{c^2}{8} + \frac{h^2}{6})$

Area of spherical surface
       = 2 π rh

       = $\pi (\frac{c^2}{4} + h^2)$

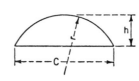

TABLE 16 — ROUNDING OF NUMBERS   155

The procedure for rounding numbers to a desired number of decimal places is shown below. The examples show numbers being rounded to 3 decimal places, but the principles illustrated apply to rounding to any number of decimal places.

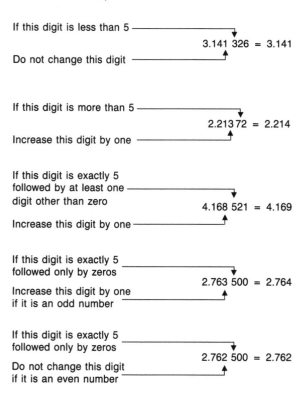

If this digit is less than 5 ──────────────┐
                                            ▼
                        3.141 326 = 3.141
                                    ▲
Do not change this digit ──────────┘

If this digit is more than 5 ──────────────┐
                                            ▼
                        2.213 72 = 2.214
                                ▲
Increase this digit by one ────┘

If this digit is exactly 5
followed by at least one ──────────────────┐
digit other than zero   ▼
                        4.168 521 = 4.169
                                ▲
Increase this digit by one ────┘

If this digit is exactly 5 ────────────────┐
followed only by zeros   ▼
                        2.763 500 = 2.764
Increase this digit by one   ▲
if it is an odd number ────────────────┘

If this digit is exactly 5 ────────────────┐
followed only by zeros   ▼
                        2.762 500 = 2.762
Do not change this digit   ▲
if it is an even number ────────────────┘

When rounding numbers to achieve whole numbers, where accuracy is not essential, employ the term (approx) to identify the loose equivalent. Example: 33 ft = 10.058 m or 10 m (approx).

Many of the symbols listed in this section are in fact abbreviations rather than symbols. For the sake of simplicity, however, the term "symbol" is used throughout, and should be understood to mean "symbol or abbreviation".

In order to save space, complex unit symbols are usually written with parentheses throughout the work rather than with exponents e.g., cubic metre per kilogram second is symbolized

$$\text{m}^3 / (\text{kg·s}) \text{ rather than } \text{m}^3\text{·kg}^{-1}\text{·s}^{-1}$$

This should not be taken to imply that the use of parentheses is preferable; the exponential form is equally acceptable.

Combinations and multiples of symbols for lenghty compound units seldom used are not always included.

Symbol	Name of unit or remarks

– A –

Symbol	Name of unit or remarks
a	are
"	atto – (10^{-18})
"	year (astronomy)
"	ab – (prefix)
amu	atomic mass unit (old)
ap, apoth	apothecaries (mass or weight)
asb	apostilb (luminance)
at	technical atmosphere
atm	physical atmosphere
av, avdp	avoirdupois (mass or weight)
A	ampere
Å	angstrom (spectrometry)
At	ampere turn (magnetomotive force)
AU	astronomical unit
A / V	ampere per volt (siemens)
A / Wb	ampere per weber ($= 1 / \text{H}$ or H^{-1})
$\text{A}^2\text{·s}^3 / (\text{kg·m}^2)$	siemens (in terms of base units)
$\text{A}^2\text{·s}^4 / (\text{kg·m}^2)$	farad (in terms of base units)
A·s / V	farad (capacitance)

– B –

Symbol	Name of unit or remarks
b	barn (atomic physics)
bar	bar (pressure)
bbl	barrel
bbl (US)	dry barrel (US)
Bi	biot (abampere)
bu	bushel
b / erg	barn per erg
b / eV	barn per electronvolt
BeV	should not be used; GeV (gigaelectronvolt) should be used instead.
b / sr	barn per steradian
b / (sr·erg)	barn per steradian erg

Bi·cm^2	biot centimetre squared
Bq	becquerel (activity of a radionuclide)
Btu	British thermal unit
Btu / h	British thermal unit per hour
Btu / lb	British thermal unit per pound
Btu / (lb·°F)	British thermal unit per pound degree Fahrenheit
Btu / (lb·°R)	British thermal unit per pound degree Rankine
Btu / (s·ft·°F)	British thermal unit per second foot degree Fahrenheit
Btu / (s·ft·°R)	British thermal unit per second foot degree Rankine

– C –

c	centi – (10^{-2})
"	centesimal minute (angle)
cc	centesimal second (angle)
"	should not be used for cubic centimetre
c / s (not cps)	cycle per second
cal$_{15}$	15° calorie
cal$_{IT}$	Int. Steam Table calorie
cal$_{tc}$ or cal$_{th}$	thermochemical calorie
Cal	large calorie or kilocalorie
cal$_{IT}$ / (g·°C)	Int. Steam Table calorie per gram degree Celsius
cal$_{IT}$ / (g·K)	Int. Steam Table calorie per gram kelvin
cm^3 not cc	cubic centimetre (millilitre)
cd	candela (base unit)
cd·sr	candela steradian (lumen)
cd·sr / m^2	candela steradian per square metre (lux)
ch	chain (surveyor or engineer)
cin	circular inch
cmil	circular mil
cmm	circular millimetre
cmHg	centimetre of mercury
cmH$_2$0	centimetre of water
cP	centipoise (dynamic viscosity)
cSt	centistokes (kinematic viscosity)
ctl	cental (mass)
C / V	coulomb per volt (farad)
CH or CV	metric horsepower
cm^{-1}	reciprocal centimetre
cwt	hundredweight (mass)
C	coulomb (ampere second)
°C	degree Celsius (not centigrade)
Ci	curie
CAN	Canada

– D –

d	deci – (10^{-1})
"	day (mean solar time)
da	deca – (10^1) or deka – (US only)
dB	decibel (sound level)
degC	use °C or degree Celsius
degK	kelvin (use K only or kelvin not °K)
dr	dram (US) or drachm (UK)
dr ap	dram apothecaries (US only)
dry pt (US)	dry pint
dry qt (US)	dry quart
dwt	pennyweight (mass)
dyn	dyne (force)
dyn / Bi^2	dyne per biot squared
dyn / (Bi·cm)	dyne per biot centimetre
dyn·cm	dyne centimetre
dyn / cm^2	dyne per square centimetre
dyn / cm^3	dyn per centimetre cubed
dyn·cm / Bi	dyne centimetre per biot
dyn / Fr	dyne per franklin
dyn·s / cm^5	dyne second per centimetre to the fifth power

– E –

emu	electromagnetic unit
esu	electrostatic unit
erg	erg (work or energy CGS system)
eV	electronvolt
eV^{-1}	reciprocal electronvolt
eV / (cm^2·s)	electronvolt per square centimetre second

– F –

f	suffix for force (kgf, lbf, etc.)
"	femto – (10^{-15})
fc	footcandle
ft·La	foot lambert
fl dr	fluid dram or fluid drachm
fl oz	fluid ounce
ft·pdl	foot poundal
Fr	franklin
ft	foot
ft^2	square foot
ft^3	cubic foot
ft·lbf	foot pound-force
ftH_2O	foot of water
ft / s	foot per second (velocity)
ft / s^2	foot per second squared (acceleration)
ft^3 / s	cubic foot per second (volume per time)
F	farad (capacitance)
°F	degree Fahrenheit

– G –

g	gram (mass)
gr (UK, US)	grain (1 / 7000 avdp lb)
...^{g}	grade (angle)
gal	gallon (CAN, UK, US)
gi	gill (US)
gf	gram-force
grf	grain-force
g·rad	gram – rad (= 10^{-5} J)
Gb	gilbert (magnetomotive force)
Gs	gauss (magnetic flux density)
Gy	gray (absorbed dose index)
GW·h	gigawatt hour

– H –

h	hour (mean solar time)
″	hecto – (10^2)
hp	horsepower (energy)
hp·h	horsepower hour
ha	hectare
Hg	mercury (pressure)
Hz	hertz (frequency)

– I –

in	inch
inHg	inch of mercury
inH$_2$0	inch of water (pressure)
in^2	square inch (area)
in^3	cubic inch (volume)
in^4	inch to the fourth power
in / s	inch per second (velocity)
in^2 / s	square inch per second

– J –

J	joule (energy)
J / Å	joule per angstrom
J / (A·s)	joule per ampere second (= volt)
J / s	joule per second (= watt)
J / (kg·s)	joule per kilogram second
J / T	Joule per tesla (= ampere square metre)

– K –

k	kilo – (10^3)
kg	kilogram (mass)
kn	knot (Int. and UK)
km	kilometre (distance)
kN	kilonewton (force)
kp	kilopond (= kgf)
kPa	kilopascal (= kN / m^2)
kgf	kilogram-force
kcal	kilocalorie (energy)
keV·cm^2 / mg	kiloelectronvolt square centimetre per kilogram
kg / (A·s^2)	kilogram per ampere second squared (= tesla)
kg·m^2 / (A·s^2)	weber (in terms of base units)
kg·m^2 / (A·s^3)	volt " " " " "
kg·^{2} / (A^2·s^2)	henry " " " " "
kg·m^2 / (A^2·s^3)	ohm " " " " "
kg·m / s^2	newton " " " " "
kg / (m·s^2)	pascal " " " " "
kg·m^2 / s^2	joule " " " " "
kg·m^2 / s^3	watt " " " " "
km / h	kilometre per hour
kg / L	kilogram per litre
kg / (m·s)	= newton second per square metre = (pascal second)
kW·h	kilowatt hour

– L –

L	litre (= cubic decimetre)
lb	pound (avdp or apoth)
lbf	pound-force
li	link (surveyor or engineer)
La	lambert (luminance)
lm	lumen (luminous flux)
lx	lux (illumination)
l·y	light year (astronomy)
lb·tr	pound, troy (apothecary)

– M –

m	milli – (10^{-3})
"	metre (base unit of length)
m^2	square metre (area)
m^3	cubic metre (volume)
mi	mile
min	minute (mean solar time)
"	minim (1 / 76 800 UK gal)
"	minim (1 / 61 440 US gal)
mb	see bar. (mb is used in meteorology instead of mbar)

mGal	milligal (acceleration)
mmHg	millimetre of mercury (pressure)
mph	mile per hour, (use mi / h)
mol	mole (amount of substance)
mpg	mile per gallon, (use mi / gal)
mμ	millimicron (= 10^{-9} m or 1 nm)
$\mu\mu$	micromicron (= 10^{-12} m or 1 pm)
μ	micro – (10^{-6})
M	mega – (10^6)
Mx	maxwell (magnetic flux)
MW·h	megawatt hour
m^2 / N	square metre per newton
m^{-1}	reciprocal metre

– N –

n	nano – (10^{-9})
nmi	nautical mile (Int.)
Np	neper (dimensionless unit = 8.69 dB)
Np / m	neper per metre
N	newton (N should not be used for normal)
N·s / m^2	newton second per square metre (= Pa·s)

– O –

Oe	oersted (magnetic field strength)
oz	ounce, avoirdupois
oz ap	ounce, apothecaries
oz apoth	ounce, apothecaries
oz t	ounce, troy
oz tr	ounce, troy

– P –

p	pico – (10^{-12})
p	pond (force)
pc	parsec (astronomy)
pdl	poundal (force)
phon	phon (loudness level)
ph	phot (illumination)
pk	peck (volume)
pt	pint (UK, US)
ppb	part per billion (should not be used)
ppm	part per million (should not be used)
Pl	poiseuille (dynamic viscosity)
psi	pound per square inch (use lbf / in^2)
psia	pound per square inch (absolute)
psig	pound per square inch (gauge)
Pa	pascal (pressure)
PS	pierdestaerke or CV (cheval vapeur)
pz	pièze (pressure = 1 kPa)
P	poise (dynamic viscosity)

– Q –

qr	quarter (mass, UK, US)
"	quarter (linear, UK)
qt	quart

– R –

r	revolution (angle)
"	roentgen (old)
R	roentgen (radioactivity)
rad	radian (angle)
rd	rad (absorbed dose)
rep	rep (absorbed dose)
rem	rem (radioactivity)
Rd	rutherford (radioactivity)
Ry	rydberg (atomic constant)
$R \cdot m^2 / (Ci \cdot h)$	roentgen metre squared per curie hour
°R	degree Rankine (temperature)
°Ré	degree Réaumur (temperature)

– S –

s	second (mean solar time)
"	stat – (prefix)
s^{-1}	reciprocal second
S	siemens (conductance)
sb	stilb (luminance)
sh cwt	hundredweight, short
sh tn	ton, short
sone	sone (loudness)
sc	scruple (apoth)
sr	steradian (solid angle)
st	stère $(= m^3)$
St	stokes (kinematic viscosity)
sn	sthène (force)
Sv	sievert (dose equivalent, radiology)

– T –

t	tonne (metric ton)
tn	ton (2000 lb)
ton	ton (2240 lb)
tc	thermochemical
th	thermie (energy)
thou	milli – inch (= mil = 25.4 μm)
torr	torr (millimetre of mercury)
tr	troy (apothecaries)
tf	tonne-force
tnf	ton-force
tonf	long ton-force
T	tera – (10^{12})
T	tesla (magnetic flux density)

– U –

u	atomic mass unit
U	enzyme unit
UK	United Kingdom
US	United States

– V –

V	volt (= W / A)
VA	volt ampere
V / A	volt per ampere (= ohm)
V·s	volt second (= weber)
V·s / A	volt second per ampere (= henry)
V·s / m²	volt second per square metre (= tesla)

– W –

W	watt (= J / s = V / A)
W / A	watt per ampere (= volt)
Wb	weber (= Volt second)
Wb / A	weber per ampere (= henry)
Wb / (A·m)	weber per ampere metre (= H / m)
Wb / m²	weber per square metre (= tesla)
W·h	watt hour
W·s	watt second (= joule)

– X –

XU	X-unit (= 1.002×10^{-4} nm)

– Y –

yd	yard (length)
yd²	square yard (area)
yd³	cubic yard (volume)

Symbols beginning with an arbitrary sign or a Greek letter

...″	minute (sexagesimal)
...″	second (sexagesimal)
...°	degree (angular)
...ʳ	revolution
...ᵍ	grade
...ᴸ	quadrant
...ᶜ	minute (centesimal)
...ᶜᶜ	second (centesimal)
°C	degree Celsius (not centigrade)
°F	degree Fahrenheit
°R	degree Rankine
°Ré	degree Réaumur
...° / s	degree per second
...ᵍ / s	grade per second
μ	micron (obsolete)
μm	micrometre
Ω	ohm
Ω^{-1}	siemens (previously mho)
Ω·s	henry
γ	gamma = 1 nT; also 1 μg
λ	lamda = 1 μL = 1 mm³

Petroleum Products

Approximate conversion factors for crude oil

Barrel	× 35	= gal (imp or UK)
"	× 42	= gal (US)
"	× 0.159	= kilolitre (m³)
'	× 0.136	= tonne (metric ton)
"	× 0.150	= ton (short)
"	× 0.134	= ton (long)
Gallon (imp or UK)	× 0.028 57	= barrel (imp or UK)
" "	× 1.201	= gal (US)
" "	× 0.004 55	= kilolitre (m³)
" "	× 0.003 91	= tonne (metric ton)
" "	× 0.004 29	= ton (short)
" "	× 0.003 83	= ton (long)
Gallon (US)	× 0.023 81	= barrel
" "	× 0.833	= gal (UK)
" "	× 0.003 785 4	= kilolitre (m³)
" "	× 0.003 25	= tonne (metric ton)
" "	× 0.003 58	= ton (short)
" "	× 0.003 19	= ton (long)
Kilolitre (m³)	× 6.289	= barrel
" "	× 220	= gal (imp or UK)
" "	× 264	= gal (US)
" "	× 0.863	= tonne (metric ton)
" "	× 0.951	= ton (short)
" "	× 0.849	= ton (long)
Ton (short)	× 6.65	= barrel
" "	× 233	= gal (imp or UK)
" "	× 279	= gal (US)
" "	× 1.05	= kilolitre (m³)
" "	× 0.907	= tonne (metric ton)
" "	× 0.893	= ton (long)
Ton (long)	× 7.45	= barrel
" "	× 261	= gal (imp or UK)
" "	× 313	= gal (US)
" "	× 1.18	= kilolitre (m³)
" "	× 1.016	= tonne (metric ton)
" "	× 1.12	= ton (short)
Tonne (metric ton)	× 7.33	= barrel
" "	× 256	= gal (imp or UK)
" "	× 308	= gal (US)
" "	× 1.16	= kilolitre (m³)
" "	× 1.102 31	= ton (short)
" "	× 0.984 205	= ton (long)

Crude oil (*)

barrel	× 0.136	=	tonne
tonne	× 7.33	=	barrel
barrel / day	× 49.8	=	tonne / year
tonne / year	× 0.0201	=	barrel / day

Gas

barrel	× 0.118	=	tonne
tonne	× 8.45	=	barrel
barrel / day	× 43.2	=	tonne / year
tonne / year	× 0.0232	=	barrel / day

Kerosene

barrel	× 0.128	=	tonne
tonne	× 7.80	=	barrel
barrel / day	× 46.8	=	tonne / year
tonne / year	× 0.0214	=	barrel / day

Gas / Diesel

barrel	× 0.133	=	tonne
tonne	× 7.50	=	barrel
barrel / day	× 48.7	=	tonne / year
tonne / year	× 0.0205	=	barrel / day

Fuel oil

barrel	× 0.149	=	tonne
tonne	× 6.70	=	barrel
barrel / day	× 54.5	=	tonne / year
tonne / year	× 0.0184	=	barrel / day

(*) based on world average gravity (excluding Natural Gas liquids)
   Source: statiscal review of the world oil industry

ADDENDA

Constants and Useful Data

Quantity	Customary Units	SI Equivalent
atmospheric pressure (std)	14.696 psi	101.325 kPa
density:		
dry air	0.075 lb / ft³ (70°F & 29.92 in Hg)	1.205 kg / m³ (20°C & 101.325 kPa)
water	62.426 lb / ft³ (39°F)	1 kg / L (4°C)
aluminum	173 lb / cu ft	2771 kg / m³
coal	79-94 lb / cu ft	1265-1506 kg / m³
copper	557 lb / cu ft	8922 kg / m³
lead	708 lb / cu ft	11 341 kg / m³
nickel	555 lb / cu ft	8890 kg / m³
steel	490 lb / cu ft	7850 kg / m³
zinc	446 lb / cu ft	7144 kg / m³
dollars per million Btu	$1.00 / 10⁶ Btu	$0.948 / GJ
expansion of steel pipe (approx)	0.75 in / 100 ft / 100°F	0.125% / 100°C
friction drop:		
compressed air piping	1 psi / 1000 ft	22.62 Pa / m
ventilation piping	1 in W.G. / 100 ft	8.17 Pa / m
water piping	1 ft / 100 ft	98.06 Pa / m
gas constant (R)	1544 ft lb / (lb mol·°R)	8.314 320 J / (mol·K)
gravity (acceleration due to – at sea level and 45° N. Lat.)	32.1740 ft / sec²	9.806 650 m / s²
gradient (pipe)	0.5" / 10 ft	4.2 mm / m
latent heat:		
fusion of ice	144 Btu / lb	335 kJ / kg
vaporisation of water	970 Btu / lb (212°F & 14.7 psia)	2256 kJ / kg (100°C & 101.325 kPa)
ton of refrigeration	12 000 Btu / hr	3.516 867 kW
velocity of light	186 272 mi / sec.	299 776 km / s
velocity of sound (dry air at 0°C)	1087.1 fps	331.3 m / s

SI Counterparts of Units to be Discoutinued

Quantity	Customary and metric units that are to be phased out	SI units and those that are permitted for use with SI
Length	inch, foot yard, mile micron angstrom	millimetre, centimetre metre, kilometre micrometre nanometre
Area	square inch, square foot square yard, acre square mile	square centimetre square metre, hectare square kilometre
Volume	cubic inch, cubic foot fluid ounce, pint quart, gallon bushel, barrel	cubic centimetre, cubic metre millilitre litre kilolitre
Mass	ounce, pound ton	gram, kilogram tonne, megagram
Temperature	degree Fahrenheit degree centigrade	degree Celsius, kelvin degree Celsius
Speed	mile per hour	kilometre per hour metre per second
Frequency	cycle per second	hertz, kilohertz, etc.
Force	pound-force kilogram-force, dyne, poundal	newton, kilonewton, etc.
Pressure	pound per square inch (psi), kilogram-force per square centimetre, torr, atmosphere, millimetre of mercury, bar	pascal, kilopascal, etc.
Energy	foot pound-force, calorie, horsepower hour, Btu, erg, therm, foot poundal	joule, kilojoule, etc.
Luminous intensity	candle	candela
Illumination	foot candle	lux
Conductance	mho	siemens

Printed in Canada